SCOTTISH PICTURES

AUCTION ENQUIRIES AND INFORMATION

SPECIALISTS IN CHARGE

Grant Ford
Tel. 020 7293 5497

Leonora Clark
Tel. 020 7293 5707

John Robertson
Edinburgh
Tel. 0131 226 7201

Anthony Weld-Forester
Glasgow
Tel. 0141 221 4817

SALE ADMINISTRATOR

Les Morris
Tel. 020 7293 5456
Fax 020 7293 5962

PRIVATE CLIENT SERVICES

*For assistance in buying
at this auction*
Karin de Besche
Tel. 020 7293 5184

TELEPHONE BIDDING

Vanessa Vermette
Tel. 020 7293 5002
Fax 020 7293 5924

ABSENTEE BIDS

David Stanley
Tel. 020 7293 5283
Fax 020 7293 6255

**24 HOUR RECORDED
INFORMATION**

*Current Auctions
and Viewing*
Tel. 020 7293 5868

Spoken Auction Results
Tel. 020 7293 5855

Faxed Auction Results
Tel. 020 7293 5959

PAYMENT

Client Account Manager
Phil Barnard
Tel. 020 7293 5761
Fax 020 7293 5926

SHIPPING

Exports
Rachel Pemberton
Tel. 020 7293 5180

Imports
June Riddell
Tel. 020 7293 6070
Fax 020 7293 5952

Kings House Warehouse
Paul Dennis
Tel. 020 8232 5600

SUBSCRIPTIONS

020 7293 6410

Single Orders
Tel. 020 7293 6444
Fax 020 7293 5909

**SOTHEBY'S
WORLD WIDE WEB SITE**

www.sothebys.com

**SOTHEBY'S
INSTITUTE OF ART**

Course Information
Tel. 020 7462 3232
Fax 020 7580 8160
education@
sothebys.com

SOTHEBY'S SPECIALISTS FOR THIS AUCTION

Scottish Pictures
Grant Ford
020 7293 5497
grant.ford@sothebys.com

Scottish Pictures
Leonora Clark
020 7293 5707
leonora.clark@sothebys.com

SCOTTISH PICTURES

SALE L01140

AUCTION

HOPETOUN HOUSE, SOUTH QUEENSFERRY, WEST LOTHIAN

Monday 9 April 2001 at 6 pm

ABSENTEE BIDS

This catalogue may be referred to as L01140 "MATADOR"

For bids only:
Up to 6 April
(London)
Tel 020 7293 5283
Fax 020 7293 6255

From 7 April
(Hopetoun House)
Tel 0131 331 4395/2612
Fax 0131 331 2268

EXHIBITION

SOTHEBY'S
34-35 NEW BOND STREET, LONDON

Thursday 29 March
9 am to 4.30 pm

Friday 30 March
9 am to 4.30 pm

Sunday 1 April
12 noon to 4 pm

Monday 2 April
9 am to 4.30 pm

EXHIBITION

HOPETOUN HOUSE, SOUTH QUEENSFERRY, WEST LOTHIAN

Saturday 7 April
10 am to 6 pm

Sunday 8 April
10 am to 5 pm

Monday 9 April
9 am to 1 pm

CATALOGUE

£14 at the gallery
£16 by mail
£18 overseas

FRONT COVER ILLUSTRATION

Lot 96
Edward Arthur Walton,
Miss Margaret Macfarlane

BACK COVER ILLUSTRATION

Lot 116
Francis Campbell Boileau Cadell,
The Matador

PRINCIPAL OFFICES WORLDWIDE

London 44 (0)20 7293 5000
New York (212) 606 7000
Los Angeles (310) 274 0340
Chicago (312) 396 9599
Paris 33 (1) 53 05 53 05
Geneva 41 (22) 908 4800
Tokyo 81 (3) 3230 2755
Hong Kong (852) 2 524 8121

CONTENTS

IMPORTANT NOTICES TO BUYERS

Notice to Buyers Resident in Scotland

Payment and clearance may be made immediately following the end of the sale. There will be NO CLEARANCE of lots from Hopetoun House on 9 April 2001. After that all lots purchased by Scottish residents will be transported to either our Glasgow office at 130 Douglas Street, Glasgow, telephone 0141 221 4817 or our Edinburgh office at 112 George Street, Edinburgh, telephone 0131 226 7201 where they will be available from 9 am on Wednesday 11 April 2001. All other lots will be available for collection from our London office from 9 am on Monday 16 April 2001.

Prospective buyers are advised to inform the Sotheby's desk in Glasgow, either prior to the sale or immediately afterwards of the preferred destination of their purchases.

In the absence of any direct instructions purchases made by East Coast buyers will be sent to our Edinburgh office, and purchases made by West Coast buyers will be available at our Glasgow office and purchases made by our Southern buyers will be made to our London office.

Notice to other Buyers

Uncollected lots will be returned to Sotheby's, 34-35 New Bond Street, London W1, for collection as from 9 am Monday 16 April 2001. Purchasers are requested to arrange clearances as soon as possible and are reminded that purchases are only insured for a period of five (5) working days following the sale. Lots will only be released to the purchaser, or his authorised representative, upon presentation of release notes issued by the cashier of Sotheby's upon settlement of all accounts.

Please note that all paintings transferred to London which are larger than 6ft by 5ft (182cm by 152cm) including the frame, will be sent to our King's House Warehouse address on Monday 16 April 2001.

Estimates in Euros

As a guide to potential buyers, estimates for this sale are also shown in Euros. The estimates printed in the catalogue in Pounds Sterling have been converted at the following rate, which was current at the time of printing. These estimates may have been rounded:

£1 = €1.57

By the date of the sale this rate is likely to have changed, and buyers are recommended to check before bidding.

During the sale Sotheby's may provide a screen to show currency conversions as bidding progresses. This is intended for guidance only and all bidding will be in Pounds Sterling. Sotheby's is not responsible for any error or omissions in the operation of the currency converter.

Payment for purchases is due in Pounds Sterling, however the equivalent amount in any other currency will be accepted at the rate prevailing on the day that payment is received in cleared funds.

Settlement is made to vendors in the currency in which the sale is conducted, or in another currency on request at the rate prevailing on the day that payment is made by Sotheby's.

2 **Erskine Nicol, R.S.A., A.R.A.**
   1825-1904
   THE GREEN EYED MONSTER
   signed and dated l.r.: *Nicol/54;*
   indistinctly inscribed on an old
   fragmented label attached to the
   reverse
   oil on canvas
   29.5 by 45cm., 11½ by 17¾in.

   £2,000-3,000
   €3,150-4,700

3 **Horatio McCulloch, R.S.A.**
   1805-1867
   MOONLIGHT LANDSCAPE
   signed l.r.: *H McCulloch*
   oil on canvas
   51 by 61cm., 20 by 24in.

   ‡ £2,000-3,000
   €3,150-4,700

4 **J.Davidson**
   19th Century
   SCOTTISH DOMESTIC SCENE
   signed and dated l.l.:
   J.DAVIDSON/1801
   oil on canvas
   45.5 by 56cm., 18 by 22in.

   £2,000-3,000
   €3,150-4,700

2

3

4

5

6

**5 Arthur Perigal, R.S.W., R.S.A.
1816-1884**
LOCH AWE
oil on canvas
76 by 122cm., 30 by 48in.

£7,000-10,000
€11,000-15,700

**6 Patrick Nasmyth
1787-1831**
THE VILLAGE FORD
signed and dated l.r.: *1830/PatK
Nasmyth*
oil on panel *Provenance:*
Sold for 370 guineas in the Henry
Jenkins Collection, Christies, 27th
March 1897
Thomas Agnew & Sons
M.Newman Ltd
28.5 by 37cm., 10¼ by 14½in.

£6,000-8,000
€9,400-12,600

7

7 Frederick Richard Lee, R.A.
1798-1879
VIEW OF BENMORE LOOKING UP GLEN
DOCHART
signed and dated l.l.: *F.R.Lee R.A.*
1851; signed, inscribed and
numbered *4* on a label attached to
the stretcher
oil on canvas
97 by 132cm., 38¼ by 52in.

£10,000-15,000
€15,700-23,500

8

8 Henry Bright
1814-1873
A VIEW OF PERTHSHIRE
signed and dated l.l.: *HBright 1851*
oil on canvas
45.5 by 76.5cm., 18 by 30in.

Provenance:
The Boydell Galleries, Liverpool

£3,000-5,000
€4,700-7,800

9

10

11

9 George W. Horlor
fl.1849-1866
IN THE HIGHLANDS
signed and dated l.l.:
G. W. Horlor/1885
oil on canvas laid down on board
61.5 by 81.5cm., 24¼ by 32in.

£4,000-6,000
€6,300-9,400

10 John Sargent Noble
1848-1896
DEER STALKING
signed l.l.: *J.S.Noble;* bears title and
date on the reverse
oil on canvas
51 by 76cm., 20 by 30in.

£2,000-3,000
€3,150-4,700

11 Archibald Thorburn
1860-1935
A WINGED MALLARD
signed and dated l.r.:
A. Thorburn/Jany.29./97
watercolour heightened with
bodycolour
46.5 by 69.5cm., 18¼ by 27½in.

Provenance:
Mawson, Swan & Morgan Ltd,
Newcastle

£3,000-4,000
€4,700-6,300

12 Edward Thornton Crawford, R.S.A.
1806-1885
TANTALLON CASTLE
indistinctly signed and dated l.l.:
Edw. T. Crawford 1847
oil on canvas
28 by 40cm., 11 by 15¾in.

£1,500-2,000
€2,350-3,150

13 William Woodhouse
1857-1939
THE DAY'S BAG
signed l.l.: *W. Woodhouse*
oil on canvas
51 by 61cm., 20 by 24in.

£12,000-18,000
€18,800-28,300

14

15

16

14 Edmund George Warren
1834-1909
FLY FISHING
signed l.r.: *Edmund E Warren*
watercolour
45 by 65.5cm., 17¾ by 25¾in.

‡ £3,000-5,000
€4,700-7,800

15 Arthur Perigal, R.S.A., R.S.W.
1816-1884
BEDDGELERT, NORTH WALES
signed and dated l.r.: *A.Perigal 1850*
oil on canvas
30.5 by 47cm., 12 by 18½in.

Exhibited:
Edinburgh, Royal Scottish Academy,
1857, no.44

£2,000-3,000
€3,150-4,700

16 Richard Ansdell, R.A.
1815-1885
RETRIEVED
signed with monogram and dated
l.r.: *1867*
oil on canvas
101 by 61cm., 40 by 24½in.

£10,000-15,000
€15,700-23,500

17 Hugh William 'Grecian' Williams
1773-1829
COTTAGES BY A LOCH AT KILBRIDE,
ARGYLL
watercolour over pencil
26 by 37cm., 10¼ by 14½in.

£1,000-1,500
€1,550-2,350

18

19

**18 Alfred de Bréanski, Senior
1852-1928**
NEAR CORRA LYNN NB
signed l.l.: *Alfred de Bréanski*; signed
and inscribed with title on the
reverse
oil on canvas
51 by 76cm., 20 by 30in.

£10,000-15,000
€15,700-23,500

**19 David Farquharson, A.R.A.,
A.R.S.A., R.S.W.
1840-1907**
THE AULD BRIG O' AYR
signed and dated l.l.: *David
Farquharson/ 86*; signed and inscribed
with title and artist's address on a
label attached to the frame
oil on canvas
40.5 by 61cm., 16 by 24in.

£7,000-10,000
€11,000-15,700

20

21

22

20 Alfred de Bréanski, Junior
1877-1957
BEN LEDI FROM THE TEITH AT
CALLENDER, PERTHSHIRE
signed l.r.: *A de Bréanski Jnr;* signed
and inscribed with title on the
reverse
oil on canvas
51 by 76cm., 20 by 30in.

† £2,000-3,000
€3,150-4,700

21 George Blackie Sticks
1843-1938
A SUMMER DAY ON THE TUMMEL;
NEAR TARBOT, LOCH FYNE, EVENING
a pair, one signed and dated l.l., the
other l.r.: *GB Sticks/1877;* (2)
20.5 by 46cm., 8 by 18in.

£2,000-3,000
€3,150-4,700

22 Alfred de Bréanski, Junior
1877-1957
NEAR GLEN URQUHART - WEST
HIGHLANDS
signed l.r.: *A.de Bréanski Jun;* signed
and inscribed with title on the
reverse
oil on canvas
41 by 61cm., 16 by 24in.

‡ £1,500-2,500
€2,350-3,900

23 Alfred de Bréanski, Senior
1852-1928
PERTHSHIRE, SCOTLAND
signed l.r.: *Alfred de Bréanski*
oil on canvas
61 by 91.5cm., 24 by 36in.

Provenance:
Cooling Galleries

£25,000-35,000
€39,200-55,000

24 Sir James Lawton Wingate
1846-1924
IN PERTHSHIRE
signed l.l.: *Wingate*
oil on canvas
35.5 by 52cm., 14 by 20½in.

£1,000-1,500
€1,550-2,350

25

26

27

25 Alfred Fontville de Bréanski
1877-1957
A HIGHLAND ROAD
signed l.l.: *A.F.de Bréanski*
oil on canvas
51 by 76cm., 20 by 30in.

£2,000-3,000
€3,150-4,700

26 David Farquharson, A.R.A.,
A.R.S.A., R.S.W.
1840-1907
A COTTAGE DOOR IN HOLLAND
signed and dated l.l.: *D Farquharson/1882*; inscribed with title l.r.
oil on canvas
30.5 by 51cm., 12 by 20in.

Provenance:
J.E.Bennett & Sons Ltd, Glasgow

£3,000-4,000
€4,700-6,300

27 David Farquharson, A.R.A.,
A.R.S.A., R.S.W.
1840-1907
DROVING CATTLE
signed and dated l.l.: *David Farquarson/1899*
oil on canvas
46 by 76cm., 18 by 30in.

£3,000-4,000
€4,700-6,300

28 James Heron
fl.1873-1919
SUMMER AFTERNOON
signed l.r.: *James Heron*; signed and indistinctly inscribed with title on the reverse
oil on canvas
62.5 by 91.5cm., 24½ by 36in.

£1,500-2,000
€2,350-3,150

29 Eugen Dekkert
b.1865
THE TIMBER WAGON
signed l.l.: *E.Dekkert*
oil on canvas
51 by 61cm., 20 by 24in.

£1,500-2,000
€2,350-3,150

30 Thomas Hunt
1854-1929
EVENING MEAL
signed l.r.: *Thos Hunt;*
gouache on paper
48.5 by 73.5cm., 19 by 29in.

£1,500-2,000
€2,350-3,150

31 Duncan McLaurin, R.S.W.
1849-1921
LET A STOUT HEART TO STEY BRING
signed and dated l.l.: *Duncan*
McLaurin 79
oil on canvas
76 by 128cm., 30 by 50in.

£2,000-3,000
€3,150-4,700

32 Robert Watson
fl.1845-1866
THE FLOCK AT REST; CATTLE IN THE
HIGHLANDS
a pair, both signed and dated l.r.: *R*
Watson/1883
oil on canvas (2)
one 61 by 92cm., 24 by 36¼in., the
other 61.5 by 97.5cm., 24¼ by
38½in.

£5,000-7,000
€7,800-11,000

33 Sir James Lawton Wingate
1846-1924
HOMEWARD BOUND
signed l.r.: *Wingate*
oil on canvas
42 by 51cm., 18½ by 20in.

£1,200-1,800
€1,900-2,850

34 W*C****
AN ALBUM OF SKETCHES DATED 1898
DEPICTING VIEWS OF SHETLAND,
ORKNEY, KINCARDINSHIRE AND
ABERDEENSHIRE
all sheets inscribed with initials and
title
watercolour and pen and ink on
paper, some heightened with
bodycolour
approximately 43 sheets
various sizes

£1,000-1,500
€1,550-2,350

30

31

32

35

36

35 Annie French
1872-1965
CAROL SINGERS
signed l.l.: *Annie French*
pen and ink and coloured wash
25.5 by 16.5cm., 10 by 6½in.

£2,000-4,000
€3,150-6,300

36 Annie French
1872-1965
... AND SHE CARRIED HER SKIRTS
watercolour with bodycolour over
pencil
13.5 by 9.5cm., 5¼ by 3¾in.

Provenance:
Archeus Fine Art, London

£2,000-3,000
€3,150-4,700

37 Erskine Nicol, R.S.A., A.R.A.
1825-1904
IN THE PIGSTY
oil on canvas laid down on panel
35.5 by 28cm., 14 by 11in.

£2,000-3,000
€3,150-4,700

38 Robert Gemmell Hutchison,
R.S.A., R.S.W.
1860-1936
THE CHICKEN COOP
signed l.l.: *Gemmell Hutchison*
oil on canvas
73.5 by 61cm., 29 by 24in.

£3,000-5,000
€4,700-7,800

39 Joseph Denovan Adam, Junior
c.1870-c.1935
BY THE FARM DOOR
signed and dated l.r.: *Denovan Adam
1885*
watercolour heightened with
bodycolour
51.5 by 34cm., 20¼ by 13½in.

£1,000-1,500
€1,550-2,350

40 Robert Gemmell Hutchison,
R.S.A., R.S.W.
1860-1936
BY THE HEARTH
signed and inscribed: *Gemmell
Hutchison/Hinze N.B.*
oil on canvas
60 by 45cm., 23¾ by 17¾in.

£2,000-3,000
€3,150-4,700

41 William Miller Frazer, R.S.A.
1864-1961
A FENLAND FARM
signed l.r.: *W.M.Frazer*; signed and
inscribed with title on a label
attached to the frame
oil on canvas
51 by 76cm., 20 by 30in.

Provenance:
Doig, Wilson and Wheatley

£2,500-3,500
€3,900-5,500

38

40

41

42

44

42 **Henry Young Alison**
1889-1972
IN THE CHERRY ORCHARD
oil on canvas
101.5 by 80cm., 40 by 31½in.

Provenance:
Aitken Dott & Son

£2,000-3,000
€3,150-4,700

43 **Joseph Henderson, R.S.W.**
1832-1908
BONNIE LASS
signed with monogram and dated
l.l.: *69*
oil on board
28 by 21cm., 11 by 8¼in.

£1,200-1,800
€1,900-2,850

44 **George W.Aikman, A.R.S.A.,**
R.S.W.
1831-1905
STRAWBERRY PICKERS
signed l.l.: *G Aikman*
oil on canvas
92 by 71cm., 36 by 28in

£2,000-3,000
€3,150-4,700

45

45 **James Whitelaw Hamilton, R.S.A.,
R.S.W.**
1860-1932
THRESHING
signed and dated l.l.:
J.Hamilton/1884
oil on canvas
40 by 57cm., 15¾ by 22½in.

£4,000-6,000
€6,300-9,400

46 **Jessie M.McGeehan**
1872-1961
IN A DUTCH HARBOUR
signed l.l.: *J McGeehan*
oil on canvas
56 by 40cm., 22 by 15¾in.

£4,000-6,000
€6,300-9,400

46

47

48

49

47 **John Henderson**
1860-1924
BY THE STREAM
signed l.r.: *John Henderson*
oil on panel
22 by 30cm., 8¾ by 11¾in.

£2,000-3,000
€3,150-4,700

48 **Joseph Morris Henderson, R.S.A.**
1864-1936
GATHERING WILD FLOWERS
signed l.l.: *J Morris Henderson;* signed
and inscribed with title on a label
attached to the stretcher
oil on canvas
40.5 by 51cm., 16 by 20in.

£2,500-3,500
€3,900-5,500

49 **Joseph Morris Henderson, R.S.A.**
1864-1936
GATHERING WILD FLOWERS
signed l.r.: *J.Morris Henderson*
oil on canvas
46 by 76cm., 18 by 30in.

£4,000-6,000
€6,300-9,400

50 **Murray J.MacDonald**
fl1887-1914
AFTER THE DAYS TOIL
signed and dated l.r.: *Murray
Macdonald 1903-4;* signed, inscribed
with title and dated on the reverse
oil on canvasboard
35.5 by 25.5cm., 14 by 10in.

£1,000-1,500
€1,550-2,350

51 **Charles Gustav Louis Phillips**
1863-1944
FISHING
signed, inscribed and dated l.l.:
*Sketch for/larger canvas/CGL Phillips
25*
oil on paper
21 by 25cm., 8¼ by 9¾in.

£1,000-1,500
€1,550-2,350

52 **Robert McGregor, R.S.A.**
1847-1922
CHILDREN IN THE GARDEN
signed l.r.: *RM^c Gregor*
oil on panel
41.5 by 51cm., 16½ by 20½in.

£5,000-7,000
€7,800-11,000

53 **William Stewart McGeorge, R.S.A.**
1861-1931
A BORDERLINE BALLAD
signed l.r.: *W S McGeorge*
oil on canvas
102 by 127cm., 40 by 50in.

This could possibly be the painting
exhibited at the Royal Scottish
Academy in 1932, no.371 entitled *'A
Border Ballad'*.

‡ £4,000-6,000
€6,300-9,400

54 **Robert Gemmell Hutchison,**
R.S.A., R.S.W.
1860-1936
WARMING BY THE FIRE
signed l.l.: *Gemmell Hutchison*
oil on canvas
49.5 by 60cm., 19½ by 23½in.

£3,000-5,000
€4,700-7,800

55 **William Watt Milne**
1865-1949
PUNTING AT HOUGHTON
oil on canvas
50 by 66.5cm., 20 by 26½in.

£1,200-1,800
€1,900-2,850

56 **William Beattie Brown, R.S.A.**
1831-1909
ON THE ESK
signed and dated l.l.: *W.Beattie
Brown/1876*
oil on canvas laid down on board
38.5 by 54.5cm., 14 by 21¼in.

£1,000-1,500
€1,550-2,350

52

53

54

57

58

59

57 John William Bottomley
1816-1900
RETURNING FROM THE MOOR
bears another signature and dated l.r.
oil on canvas
64 by 102cm., 25 by 40in.

Provenance:
A.G.Pirie, Esq., of 26 Queen's Gate,
London, his sale, Christie's, 17
November 1906, lot 79; by Fores

£5,000-7,000
€7,800-11,000

58 S. Burroughs Adams
19th century
ON THE WAY HOME; A REST ON THE
WAY
a pair, both signed with initials and
dated l.r.: one *SBA 1884;* the other
SBA 1883
oil on canvas (2)
each 47 by 72.5cm., 18½ by 28½in.

£3,000-5,000
€4,700-7,800

59 J Stewart Smith
19th century
VIEW OF EDINBURGH
signed l.l.: *JStewart Smith*
watercolour
52 by 95 cm., 20½ by 37½in.

‡ £3,000-5,000
€4,700-7,800

60 Sir James Lawton Wingate
1846-1924
SKIPNESS, SCOTLAND; THE COMING
STORM
a pair, both signed l.r.: *Wingate;* one
bears title on the reverse
oil on board (2)
each 33 by 50cm., 13 by 19¾in.

£800-1,200
€1,250-1,900

61 Joseph Morris Henderson, R.S.A.
1864-1936
HIGHLAND RIVER
signed l.l.: *J.Morris Henderson*
oil on canvas
25.5 by 35.5cm., 10 by 14in.

£1,000-1,500
€1,550-2,350

64

62 William Alfred Gibson
1866-1931
IN HOLLAND
signed l.l.: *W A Gibson;* indistinctly
signed and inscribed on a label
attached to the reverse
oil on panel
20 by 24cm., 8 by 9½in.

£1,000-1,500
€1,550-2,350

63 James Riddel, A.R.S.A., R.S.W.
1857-1928
A SUMMERS LANE, FIFE
signed l.r.: *J RIDDEL*
oil on canvas
46 by 61cm., 18 by 24in.

£1,000-1,500
€1,550-2,350

64 Robert Gemmell Hutchison,
R.S.A., R.S.W.
1860-1936
ON THE BANKS
signed l.r.: *Gemmell Hutchison*
oil on board
23 by 30.5cm., 9 by 12in.

£10,000-15,000
€15,700-23,500

65 Allan Ramsay
1852-1912
ON THE WEST WATER AT DUNLAPPIE,
EDZELL; NEAR MORRAN BRIDGE,
GLENECK
a pair, signed l.r.: *Allan Ramsay
1909*; the other signed l.l.: *Allan
Ramsay;* both indistinctly inscribed
on the reverse
oil on canvas (2)
each 30.5 by 45.5cm., 12 by 18in.

£1,200-1,800
€1,900-2,850

66 Joseph Morris Henderson, R.S.A.
1864-1936
SWIFT WATER
signed l.l.: *J.Morris Henderson*
oil on canvas
51 by 61cm., 20 by 24in.

£1,000-1,500
€1,550-2,350

67 William Bradley Lamond, R.B.A.
1857-1924
IN THE TURNIP FIELD
signed and dated l.l.: *W.B.Lamond
1890*
oil on canvas
25.5 by 35.5cm., 10 by 14in.

£1,000-1,500
€1,550-2,350

68

70

68 John N.McGhie
1867-1952
COMING ASHORE
signed l.l.: *JMᶜ Ghie*
oil on canvas
34.5 by 44.5cm., 13½ by 17½in.

£1,800-2,500
€2,850-3,900

69 John Jack
fl.1872-1891
THE HARBOUR
signed and dated l.l.: *J.Jack/1896*
oil on canvas
51 by 66cm., 20 by 26in.

£1,200-1,800
€1,900-2,850

70 Andrew Black, R.S.W.
1850-1916
ON THE BEACH
signed l.r.: *ANDREW BLACK*
oil on canvas
76 by 127cm., 30 by 50in.

£2,000-3,000
€3,150-4,700

71 David West, R.S.W.
1868-1936
LOSSIEMOUTH
signed l.r.: *DAVID WEST*
watercolour with scratching out
23.5 by 34cm., 9¼ by 13½in.

£1,000-1,500
€1,550-2,350

72 Archibald Kay, R.S.A., R.S.W.
1860-1935
THE SUNLIT SLOPES OF BEN LEDI
signed l.r.: *Archibald Kay*
oil on canvas
35.5 by 53.5cm., 14 by 21in.
together with S.J.Lamorna Birch,
The River Deveron, pen and brown
ink over pencil with watercolour (2)

£1,000-1,500
€1,550-2,350

73 James Garden Laing, R.S.W.
1852-1915
A SUMMER MORNING, AMSTERDAM;
THE FLOWER MARKET, AMSTERDAM
two, one signed l.l.: *James G.Laing,*
and bears title on a label attached to
the reverse; the other signed and
inscribed l.r.: *James
G.Laing/Amsterdam*
watercolour heightened with
bodycolour (2)
*one 22 by 28cm., 8¾ by 11in.; the
other 23.5 by 34cm., 9¼ by 13½in.*

£1,200-1,800
€1,900-2,850

75

74 Francis Patrick Martin
1883-1966
PORT BAN, IONA
signed l.r.: *FRANC P. MARTIN;*
signed and inscribed with the artist's
address on a label attached to the
reverse
oil on board
51 by 61cm., 20 by 24in.

£1,000-1,500
€1,550-2,350

75 Robert Gemmell Hutchison,
R.S.A., R.S.W.
1860-1936
BY THE ZUIDER ZEE
signed l.l.: *Gemmell Hutchison*
oil on canvas board
35.5 by 15cm., 14 by 20in.

Provenance:
W.B.Simpson, Glasgow

£15,000-20,000
€23,500-31,400

76 James McBey
1883-1959
A DUTCH HARBOUR
oil on canvas
38 by 69cm., 15 by 27¼in.

£1,500-2,000
€2,350-3,150

77 William Arthur Laurie Carrick
1879-1964
SHEEP SHEARING
signed l.r.: *Wm Arthur Carrick*
oil on board
50.5 by 35cm., 19¾ by 30¾in.

£1,500-2,000
€2,350-3,150

78 Circle of John Henry Lorimer, R.A.,
R.S.W., R.W.S.
1856-1936
SUMMER GARDEN
oil on board
52.5 by 45cm., 20¾ by 17¾in.

£1,000-1,500
€1,550-2,350

79 William Arthur Laurie Carrick
1879-1964
HARVESTING; WINTER LANDSCAPE;
THE HARBOUR; SUMMERTIME
four, two signed l.l., two signed l.r.:
Wm ARTHUR CARRICK
one oil on canvas, three oil on board
(4)
*various sizes, the largest 33.5 by
44cm., 13¼ by 17¼in.*

£2,000-3,000
€3,150-4,700

80

81

82

80 Robert Watson
c19th century
HIGHLAND CATTLE RESTING
signed and dated l.r.: *R Watson 1883*
oil on canvas
62 by 92cm., 24½ by 36in.

£3,000-4,000
€4,700-6,300

81 William Darling MacKay, R.S.A.
1844-1924
THE VILLAGE LANE
signed with initials l.r.: *WDM*
oil on canvas
30.5 by 40.5cm., 12 by 16in.

£2,000-3,000
€3,150-4,700

82 Wright Barker, R.B.A.
fl.1891-1935 d.1941
HIGHLAND CATTLE RESTING
signed and dated l.l.: *Wright Barker/1900*
oil on canvas
76 by 101.5cm., 30 by 40in.

‡ £3,000-5,000
€4,700-7,800

83 George Houston, R.S.A., R.S.W.
1869-1947
A SUNNY WINTER'S DAY
signed l.l.: *GEORGE HOUSTON*
oil on canvas
45.5 by 61cm., 18 by 24in.

£1,500-2,000
€2,350-3,150

84 Duncan Cameron
1837-1916
SUNRISE
signed l.r.: *Duncan Cameron*
oil on canvas
63 by 127cm., 24¾ by 50in.

£1,500-2,000
€2,350-3,150

85

85 **Robert Gemmell Hutchison,
R.S.A., R.S.W.
1860-1936**
PLEASURES LIGHT AS AIR
signed l.l.: *Gemmell Hutchison*
oil on panel
30.5 by 25.5cm., 12 by 10in.

Provenance:
Doig, Wilson & Wheatley

£12,000-18,000
€18,800-28,300

86

87

88

86 **Robert Weir Allan, R.S.A., R.W.S., R.S.W.**
1852-1942
A SCENE IN CUMBERLAND
signed l.r.: *Robert W.Allan*
watercolour
31.5 by 49.5cm., 12½ by 19½in.

£1,000-1,500
€1,550-2,350

87 **James Paterson, R.S.A., P.R.S.W., R.W.S.**
1854-1932
AUTUMN EVENING, COLVEND
signed l.r.: *James Paterson*
watercolour
53 by 36.5cm., 21 by 14½in.

£3,000-4,000
€4,700-6,300

88 **James Paterson, R.S.A., P.R.S.W., R.W.S.**
1854-1932
THE PENDS GATE, LOOKING
THROUGH TO DEANS COURT, ST
ANDREWS
signed l.l.: *James Paterson*
watercolour
54 by 35cm., 21¼ by 13¾in.

£2,000-3,000
€3,150-4,700

89 **George Houston, R.S.A., R.S.W.**
1869-1947
TAMAGAWA, JAPAN
signed l.r.: *GEORGE HOUSTON*;
inscribed and dated l.l.: *Tamagawa, Japan 1911*
watercolour heightened with
bodycolour
33 by 47cm., 13 by 18½in.

£1,200-1,800
€1,900-2,850

90 **Patrick William Adam, R.S.A.**
1854-1929
SUMMER GARDEN
signed l.r.: *P.W.Adam*
oil on panel
32 by 28cm., 12½ by 11in.

£1,200-1,800
€1,900-2,850

91 George Smith, R.S.A.
1870-1934
CATTLE RESTING IN THE SHADE
signed l.r.: *Geo Smith*
oil on canvas board
30.5 by 40.5cm., 12 by 16in.

Provenance:
James McClure & Sons
Malcolm Innes Gallery

£2,000-3,000
€3,150-4,700

92 George Houston, R.S.A., R.S.W.
1869-1947
LOCH AWE
signed l.r.: *GEORGE HOUSTON*
oil on canvas
46 by 61cm., 18 by 24in.

£2,000-3,000
€3,150-4,700

93 James Whitelaw Hamilton, R.S.A.,
R.S.W.
1860-1932
HARVEST MOON
signed l.r.: *J.WHITELAW*
HAMILTON
oil on canvas
43 by 56cm., 17 by 22in.

Exhibited:
London, The Fine Art Society,
March 1983

£2,000-3,000
€3,150-4,700

94 Sir David Murray, H.R.S.A., R.A.,
H.R.S.W., R.W.S.
1849-1933
ON THE LOCH
indistinctly signed and dated l.l.:
D.Murray 1872
oil on canvas laid down on panel
76 by 91.5cm., 30 by 36in.

£1,000-2,000
€1,550-3,150

95 William Stewart McGeorge, R.S.A.
1861-1931
BANKFOOT
signed l.r.:
oil on canvas laid down on board
29 by 40cm., 11½ by 15¾in.

£1,000-1,500
€1,550-2,350

91

92

93

The Property of Bryan Ferry Esq.

**96 Edward Arthur Walton, R.S.A.,
P.R.S.W., R.P., H.R.W.S., H.R.I
1860-1922**

MISS MARGARET MACFARLANE
signed l.l.: *E A Walton*
oil on canvas
149 by 97cm., 58½ by 38¼in.

Provenance:
Fine Art Society, London (1980)
Bryan Ferry Esq.

Exhibited:
Edinburgh, Royal Scottish Academy,
1901, no.219
Glasgow, Royal Glasgow Institute of
the Fine Arts, 1902, no.158 (lent by
J.L. Macfarlane)
Edinburgh, Fine Art Society, *Art in
Scotland 1800-1920*, August-
September 1980, not numbered.

Literature:
Art Journal, 1901, p.101
Studio, vol.25, 1902, p.207,
illustrated p.208
Fiona Macsporran, *Edward Arthur
Walton 1860-1922*, Glasgow, 1987,
p.64, illd as col. pl.9 between pp.59
and 60

£150,000-200,000
€235,000-314,000

Edward Arthur Walton and his wife

Edward Arthur Walton's portrait of
Margaret Macfarlane shows her as a
girl aged about twelve or thirteen,
wearing a white dress and white silk
dancing shoes. Her long hair is tied
at the back of her head with white
ribbons. The interior space that she
occupies is sombre and loosely
defined: a curtain hangs on the right
side, before which is placed a vase of
hydrangeas or chrysanthemums. She
sits in an elaborately carved wooden
chair, over which has been thrown a
drape of blue satin. The wall behind
her is a tobacco colour, and rises
from a white-painted skirting board.

E.A. Walton was one of the leading
Scottish painters of his generation,
specialising in portraits and
landscape subjects. His family
originated in Manchester, but his
father moved to Renfrewshire, where
Walton himself was born. After a
brief period of training in Düsseldorf
when he was just seventeen, he
returned to Glasgow where he
enrolled in the School of Art. There
he met and became friends with
James Guthrie and Joseph Crawhall,
with whom Walton and other young
artists including George Henry and
John Lavery were later to form the
loose association which came to be
known as the Glasgow Boys. In 1879
Walton worked at Rosneath,
painting landscape subjects in
company with Crawhall and
Guthrie, while from 1881 onwards
the same group along with Henry
spent periods working at Brig
O'Turk and at Cockburnspath. Of
the Glasgow Boys, and Walton's
place within the group, James Caw
wrote that 'amongst the leaders there
were half-a-dozen men who
possessed that first hand and
immediate apprehension of life and
nature which cannot be imitated
because a personal and inalienable
gift. Of these Mr E.A. Walton was
one of the chief, and even now, after
seven or eight years' residence in
London, he cannot be dissociated
from his early connections.' ('A
Scottish Painter: E.A. Walton,
A.R.S.A.', *Studio*, vol.26, 1902,
pp.161-70)

Walton's works were seen in
exhibitions in London and in
Scotland from the start of the 1880s;
he sent a work entitled *The Bend in
the River* to the Royal Scottish
Academy in 1880, and this was
followed by a succession of
landscapes and rustic subjects set in
Scotland and England including a
series done in Broadway in the
Cotswolds. In 1885 Walton sent
works to the Royal Academy in
London from an address in Stow-on-
the-Wold. This was the period when
the American painter John Singer
Sargent was living and working in
Broadway; no contact between
Walton and Sargent is referred to in
the literature, but it is tempting to
think that the two might have
known one another. The
establishment in London in 1891 of
the Society of Portrait Painters, and
the gradual elevation of the perceived
importance of portraiture as a genre
(a reappraisal led by James Whistler
who had turned to portraiture from
the 1870s onwards), along with the
enormous financial rewards that
accrued to the artists who succeeded
in gratifying the aristocratic and
bourgeois clientele of the day,
encouraged many painters to
establish themselves as portraitists in
London. Walton himself had a
studio in Cheyne Walk in Chelsea
from 1894 until about 1904.

James Whistler was the artist who
Walton most revered and who more
than any other influenced Walton's
style of portrait painting. Walton's
first contact with Whistler had
occurred in about 1891 when he
wrote to ask whether Whistler's
famous portrait of Thomas Carlyle
(Glasgow City Art Gallery), which
had first been seen at the 1877
Grosvenor Gallery exhibition, might
still be for sale and, if it were,
whether Whistler would allow a
subscription to be raised on behalf of
city of Glasgow to buy it. This
tribute on the part of a group of
young artists to one who was
described as 'a demi-god in the eyes
of the [Glasgow] Boys' (Roger

Billcliffe, *The Glasgow Boys - The Glasgow School of Painting 1875-1895*, London, 1985, p.31) was welcomed wholeheartedly by the American artist, who seems to have felt that his innovations of style and aesthetic refinement were at last being appreciated. Whistler took a particular delight in the fact that the Carlyle portrait would form part of a public collection in Scotland rather than in England, where he felt there was little sympathy for what he had been attempting. Whistler and Walton maintained close artistic relations throughout the 1890s, as is demonstrated by Whistler's having called on Walton to join him in the establishment of the International Society, which was to be a new and radical association of painters of all nationalities and which was set up during the winter of 1897-8. Even in the last year of Whistler's life Walton continued to visit him in his studio, apparently finding him on one occasion in 1902 dressed in an overcoat over his nightclothes.

From 1899 to 1904 painting, watercolours and engravings by Whistler were exhibited at the Royal Scottish Academy in Edinburgh. It seems likely that Walton may have had a role in organising these displays, which proved to be an inspiration to a number of Scottish artists of Walton's generation. James Caw, writing in 1902, gave the following account of Whistler's importance to Scottish painters in the last years of the century: 'The influence of Mr Whistler was by this time beginning to be more felt in Glasgow, and with it there came a greater desire to secure refinement of execution and design. The feeling for it was Walton's already, for within the vigour of his presentments of people and landscapes, one felt that a fine spirit was at work; acquaintance with Whistler's exquisite art brought it more obviously to the surface, and gave it a more definite direction.' (James Caw, 'A Scottish Painter: E.A. Walton, A.R.S.A.', *Studio*, vol.26, 1902, pp.161-70)

Comparison may be made between Walton's portrait of Margaret Macfarlane and a succession of paintings by Whistler. In terms of the choice of colour, the subdued and sombre range of browns and greens that form the background of the portrait by Walton echoes the deliberate manipulation of a narrow range of tints by Whistler in paintings such as *Harmony in Grey and Green: Miss Cicely Alexander* (Tate Gallery, London) (which was repeatedly exhibited in London and elsewhere in the 1890s). A motif that seems conspicuously Whistlerian in the present portrait is the section of skirting board that appears on the left side of the composition, and the length of picture rail or frieze at the top of the wall. These rectilinear elements are reminiscent in their abstract pictorial importance of the arrangement of the backgrounds of the great series of Whistler portraits of the early 1870s: *Arrangement in Grey and Black: Portrait of the Artist's Mother* (Musée d'Orsay, Paris), *Arrangement in Grey and Black, No.2: Portrait of Thomas Carlyle* (Glasgow Museum and Art Gallery) (the painting which as has been seen Walton was instrumental in buying for Glasgow), and once again *Miss Cicely Alexander*. That Margaret Macfarlane is dressed entirely in white is again a device that Walton may have borrowed from his mentor, with the purpose of separating her figure from the larger composition as well as to give symbolic emphasis to the innocence and purity of one who is still a child. In this Walton may have been consciously referring to Whistler's *Symphony in White, No.1: The White Girl* (National Gallery of Art, Washington DC), of 1862, or *The Little White Girl* (Tate Gallery, London), of 1864, a painting that was much exhibited in the 1890s and which Walton may have known in the collection of the painter Arthur Haythorne Studd.

Walton's portraits were consistently admired by critics, and particular praise was reserved for his pictures of children. A work entitled *Girl in Brown* (Neue Pinakothek, Munich), first seen at the New English Art Club in 1889, aroused great interest, and was praised by James Caw in 1894 for its 'dignified design, subtle modelling, rich colour, and masterly workmanship, or the sweetness and naiveté of girlhood expressed in face and figure.' ('A Phase of Scottish Art', *Art Journal*, 1894, pp.75-80) Caw regarded the painting of the hands as key to the success of Walton's painting of young girls: 'very noticeable ... is the beautiful way in which the hands are treated; they are drawn and modelled as if he loved to paint them, and often add very considerably to the character expression.' The careful placing and most delicate treatment of the hands in the present portrait is one of it subtle and yet expressive aspects. The portrait of Margaret Macfarlane was praised when first it appeared in an exhibition, in Edinburgh in 1901: the *Art Journal* referring to Walton's 'graceful portrait of a girl' as one of the 'outstanding works in the exhibition' (*Art Journal*, 1901, pp.100-101). When the work appeared for a second time, at the Royal Glasgow Institute in 1902, it received unreserved praise in *Studio*, being described as 'one of the most charming portraits in the exhibition': 'Seldom has Mr Walton painted a more beautiful portrait, good as a work of art, and fine as a rendering of the elusive charm of childhood. Needless to say the relative tones of the work are exquisitely balanced - that is almost always the case with Mr Walton's work - and the drawing is good and the colour sweet as well.' ('Studio-Talk', *Studio*, pp.199-217)

97 Robert Russell MacNee
1880-1952
HARVESTING
signed and dated l.l.: *RRussell*
MacNee
oil on canvas
40.5 by 61cm., 16 by 24in.

£3,000-5,000
€4,700-7,800

98 George Houston, R.S.A., R.S.W.
1869-1947
LOCH FYNE
signed l.r.: *GEORGE HOUSTON*
oil on canvas
71.5 by 91.5cm., 28 by 36in.

£3,000-5,000
€4,700-7,800

99 James Paterson, R.S.A., P.R.S.W.,
R.W.S.
1854-1932
SEASCALE
signed, inscribed with title and dated
l.l.: *James Paterson/Seascale/1889*
watercolour over pencil
24 by 34cm., 9½ by 13½in.

£1,500-2,000
€2,350-3,150

100 George Blackie Sticks
1843-1938
THE SEA BIRD'S HAUNT
signed with monogram and dated
l.l.: *86*
oil on canvas
77 by 102cm., 30¼ by 40¼in.

£1,500-2,000
€2,350-3,150

101 David Fulton, R.S.W.
fl.1880-1929
KYLES OF BUTE FROM KAMES
signed l.l.: *DAVID FULTON*
oil on canvas
30.5 by 40.5cm., 12 by 16in.

£1,000-1,500
€1,550-2,350

97

98

99

102

103

104

102 **Archibald Kay, R.S.A., R.S.W.**
1860-1935
THE 'WINDSOR CASTLE' OFF
GREENOCK
signed l.r.: *Archibald Kay R.S.W.*;
inscribed l.l.: *THE CLYDE*
oil on panel
24 by 34.5cm., 9½ by 13½in.

Provenance:
T & R Annan & Sons Ltd

£2,000-3,000
€3,150-4,700

103 **James Paterson, R.S.A., P.R.S.W.,**
R.W.S.
1854-1932
SKYE
signed l.l.: *James Paterson*
oil on panel
26.5 by 34.5cm., 10½ by 13½in.

Provenance:
Langton Gallery Limited

£3,000-4,000
€4,700-6,300

104 **George Houston, R.S.A., R.S.W.**
1869-1947
VIEW OF ARRAN; LOCH TAY
a pair, both signed l.l.: *GEORGE*
HOUSTON
oil on canvas (2)
45.5. by 61cm., 18 by 24in.

Provenance:
James McClure & Son.

£3,000-5,000
€4,700-7,800

105 **William A.Wilson, O.B.E., R.S.A.,**
R.S.W.
1905-1972
THE HARBOUR
signed and dated l.r.: *W.Wilson 1945*
watercolour heightened with
bodycolour over pencil
38 by 50.5cm., 15 by 20in.

£1,200-1,800
€1,900-2,850

106 **Robert Gemmell Hutchison,
R.S.W., R.S.A.
1855-1936**
ON THE BEACH
signed l.r.: *Gemmell Hutchison*
oil on canvas laid down on board
25.5 by 35.5cm., 10 by 14in.

‡ £5,000-7,000
€7,800-11,000

107 **John N.McGhie
1867-1952**
IN THE EAST NEUK OF FIFE
signed l.l.: *JMᶜ Ghie*
oil on canvas
51 by 61cm., 20 by 24in.

£4,000-6,000
€6,300-9,400

108 **Joseph Morris Henderson, R.S.A.
1864-1936**
THE AYRSHIRE COAST
signed l.l.:
oil on canvas
49.5 by 75cm., 19½ by 29½in.

£3,000-5,000
€4,700-7,800

109 **William A.Wilson, O.B.E., R.S.A.,
R.S.W.
1905-1972**
THATCHING THE HOUSE; THE VILLAGE
CHURCH; OUTHOUSES
three, two signed l.r.: *W.Wilson*
watercolour over pencil (3)
*one 35.5 by 48cm., 14 by 19in.;
another 36.5 by 49cm., 14½ by
19¼in.; another 35.5 by 43cm., 14 by
17in.*

£2,000-3,000
€3,150-4,700

110 **Murray J.MacDonald
fl.1887-1914**
FISHING AT LOCH LEVEN, NEAR
MARKINCH
signed and dated l.r.: *Murray
Macdonald/1891*
oil on canvas laid down on panel
28 by 40.5cm., 11 by 16in.

£1,000-1,500
€1,550-2,350

106

107

108

111

112

111 **Francis Campbell Boileau Cadell,**
R.S.A., R.S.W.
1883-1937
INTO THE GARDEN
oil on canvas board
30.5 by 23cm., 12 by 9in.

£6,000-8,000
€9,400-12,600

112 **Margaret Morris**
fl.c.1924-c.1950
SPRING IN CARLYLE SQUARE
signed with initials on reverse;
signed, inscribed with title and dated
on a label attached to the reverse
oil on board
24 by 19cm., 9½ by 7½in.

£4,000-6,000
€6,300-9,400

113

113 **John Duncan Fergusson, R.B.A.**
1874-1961
SUPINE NUDE - 1908
heavy pencil on paper
22.5 by 30.5cm., 8¾ by 12in.

£2,500-3,500
€3,900-5,500

114 **John Duncan Fergusson, R.B.A.**
1874-1961
SELF PORTRAIT AGED 26 - EDINBURGH
1900
pencil, unframed
12.5 by 11cm., 5 by 4¼in.

Provenance:
Harry (Henri Hector) McColl
Estate, Paris

£1,000-1,500
€1,550-2,350

114

The Property of a Lady

115 George Leslie Hunter
1877-1931

STILL LIFE WITH FLOWERS AND FRUIT

signed l.r.: *L Hunter*

oil on board

68.5 by 56cm., 27 by 22in.

The book 'Introducing Leslie Hunter', by T.J. Honeyman, 1937 accompanies this lot.

Provenance:

Alex Reid and Lefevre Ltd, Glasgow

£25,000-35,000

€39,200-55,000

Portrait of George Leslie Hunter

This painting is undoubtedly one of Hunter's finest still lifes from circa 1925. It has all the classic elements that differentiate Hunter's art from his fellow Colourists. The innate sense of harmony, the unusual mixture of motifs and shapes, the contrast between the weight of the fruit and the soft texture of the roses and, the incredibly complex array of colour and decoration which simply assaults the eye.

Throughout his artistic development, Hunter had three major influences at work in his paintings. Early on and in common with his fellow Colourists, Peploe, Fergusson and Cadell, he was pre-occupied with Impressionist artist, Manet's building-up of form through the skilful use of fluid or loaded brushstrokes. By 1919 however, Hunter was at last able to translate his understanding of Cezanne's theory of vibrating colour chords not only to create form but to convey the essence of nature itself. By the time of his 1923 exhibition in Glasgow, Hunter's work was beginning to gain a measure of success although typically Hunter was unable to rest on his laurels.

With the memory of an earlier trip to Paris still fresh in his mind, Hunter felt strongly that he wanted to experiment more with his sense of line and spent most of 1924 playing with this concept. Dramatically in 1925 a third major influence affected Hunter's direction. He was seduced by Matisse's latest still lifes and figures in interiors then on view in Paris. Hunter's subsequently strived to translate how volume gives way to flat plane and economy of line. Ironically it took a further three years in the Cote d'Azur and his final two years in Glasgow, before he resoundingly achieved this.

Still Life with Flowers and Fruit exposes these conflicting concepts in a brilliant display of lively brushwork, vivid colour and intuitive sense of design. Interestingly Hunter is able to lose his sense of volume in the fruit, fruit dish or vase yet the bold dark lines act to divide the pictorial design into flatter planes. Colour as always is confidently juxtaposed between cool and warm areas, sometimes to highlight form, sometimes to compliment areas of flat space.

In December 1925, Hunter had a successful exhibition at Alexander Reid in Glasgow. For once the critic for the Glasgow Herald writes in genuine delight, 'Like all progressive artists, Hunter's art has advanced stage by stage until he has now evolved a style of his own, which in its compelling power and decoration and realistic elements is well in advance of anything he has hitherto achieved.' The still lifes are described as, '..strong and striking in design and gorgeous in their colour harmonies. His favourite theme in this connection is a vase of flowers or a dish of fruit set against a richly patterned curtain.' (Glasgow Herald, 17th December 1925).

It has often been asserted that the Colourist's palette lightened and became more daring after time spent in South of France with its brilliant light. Such an assertion has ignored the facts and specifically in Hunter's case, nothing could be further from the truth.

Still Life with Flowers and Fruit clearly demonstrates the opposite is true - it was completed a year before he moved to the South of France. Hunter's colour, composition and harmony are a wonderful amalgamation of his own creativity, vision and unique understanding of modern art, how it functions and what it represents. In 1924 the Four Scottish Colourists exhibited in Paris as *Les Pentres de L'Ecosse Moderne* at the Calerie Barbazagnes. The French praised the modernity of their art and berated their own artists for lack of direction. The French Government brought paintings by Peploe and Fergusson, although Hunter had to wait until the 1931 exhibition to receive that recognition.

Still Life with Flower and Fruit confidently proclaims Hunter's special contribution to the modern movement and ultimately delivers an intensely beautiful and timeless painting.

115

116 Francis Campbell Boileau Cadell,
R.S.A., R.S.W.
1883-1937
THE MATADOR
signed l.l.: *F.C.B.Cadell*
oil on canvas
112 by 86.5cm., 44 by 34in.

Provenance:
Purchased by Alexander Mackay in
1914,
thence by descent to the present
owner

£80,000-120,000
€126,000-131,400

Portrait of Francis Campbell
Boileau Cadell

As a painting *The Matador* is a tour de force which embodies all that is exciting about Cadell's pre-World War I paintings. A portrait with a witty story, it is a superb example of Cadell's instinctive, flowing Impressionist brushwork, its composition is at once Edwardian yet also a typical Impressionist subject delivered with such modern panache that above all it is sophisticated and exuberant. The qualities inherent in this picture reveal as much of Cadell's character as it does in defining what constitutes Scottish Colourist art. In Cadell's case, the man and the artist are inseparable.

The Matador was painted in 1913 when Cadell, aged 30 years, was just beginning to establish himself as a professional artist. His early artistic talent proclaimed his wonderful sensitivity to colour, texture and form. He also displayed a graphic talent for comic satirical drawings. On the advice of a close family friend, artist and Glasgow Boy, Arthur Melville (1855-1904) and in an astonishing act of faith, Cadell's mother took him and his younger sister to live in Paris between 1899 and 1902. Only 16 years old, Cadell trained at the various studios including the Academie Julien where fellow Colourist, Samuel John Peploe studied and of course there was plenty of Impressionist work on display in the various galleries.

However it was not until 1910 and a visit to Venice that his deep love affair with vivid colour was truly released. There, his superb fluid brushwork melded with his innate sense of affluence and enjoyment to produce café scenes, canal views and architecture filled with confidence and verve. From this point on, Cadell's pictures take on a new and significant stylishness being shown at the prestigious Edinburgh art dealers, Aitken Dott, where sadly the paintings were not well received. He did not exhibit again with another dealer until after 1917.

Cadell lived life to the full. With an appetite for good food and wine he was also a generous host who loved entertaining his friends. Flamboyant by nature with a stylish sense of dress, fellow artist Stanley Curister aptly described how '..he walked with a certain jauntiness of step - a straight and serviceable pipe gripped firmly in his teeth, an eye that lifted to a twinkle and a smile ready to expand to a quick laugh; careful in dress but seldom without a gay, distinctive note - shepherd tartan trousers - a blue scarf - a yellow waistcoat - or all the glory of his kilt, but with all - an air!' (Memorial Exhibition Catalogue, Stanley Cursiter, National Gallery of Scotland, April 1942).

Continued

Cadell's social life and interesting mix of elegant and affluent friends therefore allowed him an unusual freedom to flourish artistically. By 1911, he was sufficiently popular to attract nine portrait commissions. Also about this time he began painting a series on the theme of *Lady in a Black Hat,* a subject which fascinated him for the next fifteen years. Miss Don Wauchope, notable beauty with a taste for fine clothes, was a favourite sitter. Undoubtedly *The Matador* has a certain affinity with these early essays in pose and ambience.

And what of the sitter, Alexander Mackay (1856-1936), the subject of *The Matador.* The mixture of personality, wit, costume, fun and good living makes this picture stand out. Mackay was a Dundee businessman, major shareholder and eventually a director of the Matador Land and Cattle Company. The company was formed in 1882 to provide venture capital for expanding U.S. settlements particularly in Texas. It was a peculiarly Dundee enterprise where the thriving jute industries and other wealthy individuals successfully invested their surplus capital. By the time this portrait was painted Mackay, aged 57 years, was a wealthy man and no doubt Cadell met him through his gregarious social life. Mackay was known to have a youthful apearance.

Dressing-up was also a late nineteenth century subject for many an establsed painter as a glance at Royal Scottish Academy and Glasgow Institute catalogues will attest to as late as 1910. Of course other precedents exist, interestingly as deeply rooted in French Impressionist subject matter (entertainment, crème de menthe, lavish costume for example) as in the elegant late Victorian and Edwardian portraits by Whistler, Sargent and notably Lavery and Melville (all of whom Cadell admired).

It appears that Cadell exhibited an oil sketch of this portrait a year earlier in 1912, entitled *El Chulo* in the first Society of Eight exhibition at the New Gallery in Edinburgh. The Society of Eight, formed by Cadell and other leading artists, allowed them to display their work unrestricted by dealers' considerations. Significantly Cadell always exhibted what he considered his best work there. The title is yet another intriguing clue to the flavour of the painting. Unlike today's more unpleasant connotation, in Cadell's day *El Chulo* was Spanish for a person who was egotistical, or proud of their position; it implies a certain Latin strutting. Alexander Mackay dressed in a matador costume alluding to his company name, while posturing elegantly at a mantelpiece, a glass of crème de menthe at his elbow is clearly a bit of fun that only Cadell could have succeeded in.

While it reflects the elegant sometimes foppish society which Cadell enjoyed so much in Edinburgh, *The Matador* is equally a brilliant and stylish portrait. As a Colourist painting its daring is amply displayed in the confident application of vivid colour and enjoyment of paint as a means unto itself.

117

118

117 John Duncan Fergusson, R.B.A.
1874-1961
THE ARTIST'S MOTHER, CHRISTINA,
AGED 56 - EDINBURGH C.1900
pencil, unframed
11.5 by 11cm., 4½ by 4¼in.

Provenance:
Harry (Henri Hector) McColl
Estate, Paris

£1,000-1,500
€1,550-2,350

118 John Duncan Fergusson, R.B.A.
1874-1961
THE ARTIST'S FATHER, JOHN, AGED 61
- EDINBURGH C.1900
pencil, unframed
11.5 by 10cm., 4¾ by 4in.

Provenance:
Harry (Henri Hector) McColl
Estate, Paris

£1,000-1,500
€1,550-2,350

119

119 John Duncan Fergusson, R.B.A.
1874-1961
THE ARTIST'S PARENTS, JOHN AND
CHRISTIAN, AGED 58 AND 63 -
EDINBURGH 1902
pencil
10 by 11.5cm., 4 by 4½in.

Provenance:
Harry (Henri Hector) McColl
Estate, Paris

£1,000-1,500
€1,550-2,350

120

121

122

120 John Maclaughlan Milne, R.S.A.
1886-1957
THE MOUNTAINS
signed l.l.: *Maclaughlan Milne*
oil on board
38 by 45.5cm., 15 by 18in.

£5,000-7,000
€7,800-11,000

121 John Maclaughlan Milne, R.S.A.
1886-1957
A WALLED GARDEN
signature heightened l.l.
oil on board
49.5 by 59.5cm., 19½ by 23½in.

£4,000-6,000
€6,300-9,400

122 John Maclaughlan Milne, R.S.A.
1886-1957
COTTAGES BY THE SHORE
signed l.r.: *Maclaughlan Milne*
oil on board
37.5 by 45.5cm., 14¾ by 18in.

£6,000-8,000
€9,400-12,600

123 Sir William George Gillies, R.S.A.,
R.A.
1898-1973
EYEMOUTH; PITTENWEEM; THE ROAD
TO YORKSTOWN
three, one signed and inscribed with
title l.l.: *WGillies*; another signed l.r.:
WGilles; the other signed l.l.:
WGillies
two pencil; the other pen and ink (3)
one 23.5 by 27cm., 9¼ by 10¾in.;
another 29.5 by 56cm., 11¾ by 22in.;
the other 20.5 by 24cm., 8 by 9½in.

‡ £1,500-2,000
€2,350-3,150

124 David Young Cameron, R.A., R.S.A., R.W.S., R.S.W.
1865-1945
OSTIA
signed l.l.: *DYCameron*
oil on canvas
43 by 56cm., 17 by 22in.

Exhibited:
Edinburgh, Fine Art Society, *David Young Cameron 1865-1945*, September to October 1990, no.14

£5,000-7,000
€7,800-11,000

125 David Young Cameron, R.A., R.S.A., R.W.S., R.S.W.
1865-1945
BERWICK BRIDGE FROM THE WEST
oil on canvas
15 by 35.5cm., 6 by 14in.

£2,500-3,500
€3,900-5,500

126 David Young Cameron, R.A., R.S.A., R.W.S., R.S.W.
1865-1945
THE PASS, GLENCOE
signed with initials l.r.: *D.Y.C.*;
signed and inscribed with title on the reverse
oil on board
16.5 by 24.5cm., 6½ by 9¾in.

£3,000-4,000
€4,700-6,300

127 William Page Atkinson Wells
1872-1923
THE FIELDS
indistinctly signed l.r.: *William Wells*
oil on canvas
30.5 by 45.5cm., 12 by 18in.

£2,000-3,000
€3,150-4,700

124

125

126

128

129

130

**128 David Young Cameron, R.A.,
R.S.A., R.W.S., R.S.W.
1865-1945**
BERWICK BRIDGE
signed l.r.: *DYCameron*
watercolour over pencil
24.5 by 34.5cm., 9¾ by 13½in.

Provenance:
Mr and Mrs Bill Smith

Exhibited:
Edinburgh, Fine Art Society, *Spring
'87*, 1989, no.81

£2,000-3,000
€3,150-4,700

**129 Alexander Ignatius Roche, R.S.A.
1861-1921**
POLPERRO HARBOUR
signed l.l.: *Alexander Roche*
oil on panel
26.5 by 37cm., 10½ by 14½in.

Exhibited:
London, Fine Art Society, February
1991, no.192

£1,500-2,000
€2,350-3,150

**130 James McIntosh Patrick, R.S.A.
1907-1998**
KIRKTON OF NEWTYLE
signed l.r.: *Mᶜ INTOSH/PATRICK*
watercolour over pencil
51.5 by 52cm., 20¼ by 20½in.

£4,000-6,000
€6,300-9,400

131 Stephen Bone
1904-1958
HARLECH CASTLE; FIGURE SKETCH ON
VERSO
signed l.l.: *Stephen Bone;* signed and
inscribed with title on the reverse
oil on board
33 by 41cm., 13 by 16in.

£1,500-2,000
€2,350-3,150

132 James McBey
1883-1959
HARVESTING NEAR ABERDEEN
oil on canvas
37.5 by 70cm., 14¾ by 27½in.

£1,500-1,800
€2,350-2,850

133 Jeka Kemp
1876-1966
MENTON
signed l.l.: *JEKA KEMP;* bears
signature and title on the reverse
oil on board
38 by 45.5cm., 15 by 18in.

£2,000-3,000
€3,150-4,700

134 James McIntosh Patrick, R.S.A.
1907-1998
A COUNTRY ROAD
signed l.r.: *Mᶜ INTOSH/PATRICK*
watercolour over pencil
17 by 25cm., 6¾ by 9¾in.

£1,200-1,800
€1,900-2,850

131

132

133

135

136

135 James McIntosh Patrick, R.S.A.
1907-1998
HIGH SUMMER
signed l.l.: *M^cINTOSH/PATRICK*
oil on canvas
51 by 61cm.; 20 by 24in.

‡ £5,000-7,000
€7,800-11,000

136 Sir Herbert James Gunn, R.A.,
R.S.W.
1893-1964
THE HILLS NEAR RHONDA
signed and inscribed with title on the
reverse
oil on board
36.5 by 25cm., 14¼ by 9¾in.

Provenance:
London, Fine Art Society, May 1989

£2,000-3,000
€3,150-4,700

137

137 **Edward Atkinson Hornel**
     1864-1933
     BRIGHOUSE BAY
     signed and dated l.r.: *EAHornel/1917*
     oil on canvas laid down on board
     42 by 52cm., 16½ by 20½in.

     Provenance:
     W.B.Simpson, Glasgow

     £8,000-12,000
     €12,600-18,800

138 **Francis H.Newbury, R.W.A.**
     1885-1946
     DAISY WILSON
     signed with monogram l.r.
     oil on canvas
     61 by 36.5cm., 24 by 14¼in.

     Exhibited:
     The Glasgow Girls, Kelvingrove,
     1990

     £2,000-3,000
     €3,150-4,700

138

139 one of a pair

139 one of a pair

140

139 Daivd Barrogill Keith
1891-1979
J.TAITS SHOP, KIRKWALL; BROAD
STREET KIRKWALL
a pair, inscribed with title and
signature on a label attached to the
reverse
oil on canvas board (2)
each 35.5 by 45.5cm., 14 by 18in.

£2,000-3,000
€3,150-4,700

140 James Stuart Park
1862-1933
ROSES
signed twice l.r.: *Stuart Park*
oil on canvas
51 by 61cm., 20 by 24in.

£2,000-3,000
€3,150-4,700

141 Anne Redpath, R.S.A., A.R.A.
1895-1965
PHARMACY
watercolour with gouache over
pencil
27.5 by 36.5cm., 10¾ by 14½in.

£1,000-1,500
€1,550-2,350

142 James Stuart Park
1862-1933
RED AND WHITE ROSES
oil on canvas
53 by 47cm., 21 by 18½in.

£1,500-2,000
€2,350-3,150

143 Alick Riddell Sturrock, R.S.A.
1885-1953
EVENING, CORFE
signed l.l.: *ARSturrock*
oil on canvas
51 by 61cm., 20 by 24in.

£1,000-1,500
€1,550-2,350

144 Mary Nicol Neill Armour, R.S.A., R.S.W.
b.1902
STILL LIFE WITH A GLASS
signed and dated l.l.: *50 MARY ARMOUR;* signed, inscribed with title and artist's address on a label attached to the reverse
oil on panel
37 by 52cm., 14½ by 20½in.

Provenance:
James McClure & Son

‡ £4,000-6,000
€6,300-9,400

144

145 Mary Nicol Neill Armour, R.S.A., R.S.W.
b.1902
FUCHSIA AND ROSE
signed l.l.: *Mary Armour'65*; signed and inscribed with title and artist's address on an exhibition label attached to the backboard
watercolour heightened with bodycolour
44.5 by 55.5cm., 17½ by 21¾in.

Exhibited:
Royal Society of Painters in Watercolour

£4,000-6,000
€6,300-9,400

145

146 Elizabeth Violet Blackadder, R.A., R.S.A., R.S.W.
b.1931
LANDSCAPE WITH SHEEP I
signed l.r.: *E.V.Blackadder*; signed and inscribed with title on the backboard
watercolour with bodycolour, black crayon and pencil
40 by 49.5cm., 15¾ by 19½in.

Provenance:
Aitken Dott & Son

‡ £2,000-3,000
€3,150-4,700

146

147

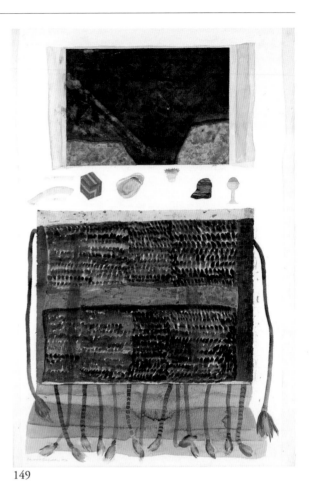

149

147 Elizabeth Violet Blackadder, R.A., R.S.A., R.S.W.
b.1931
SUNFLOWERS AND A CAT
signed, and inscribed l.l.: *Elizabeth Blackadder/Saturday 6th October 1979*
watercolour
80 by 59cm., 31½ by 23in.

Provenance:
Mercury Gallery

£6,000-8,000
€9,400-12,600

148 No lot

149 Elizabeth Violet Blackadder, R.A., R.S.A., R.S.W.
b.1931
ABSTRACT
signed and dated l.l.: *Elizabeth Blackadder 1972*
watercolour with pencil, unframed
104 by 70cm., 41 by 27½in.

‡ £3,000-4,000
€4,700-6,300

150 William Marshall Brown, R.S.A., R.S.W.
1863-1936
CONCARNEAU BOATS
signed l.r.: *Marshall Brown*
oil on canvas
35.5 by 46cm., 14 by 18¼in.

‡ £3,000-5,000
€4,700-7,800

151 William Marshall Brown, R.S.A., R.S.W.
1863-1936
CONCARNEAU MEN
signed l.r.: *Marshall Brown*
oil on canvas
30.5 by 40.5cm., 12 by 16in.

‡ £3,000-5,000
€4,700-7,800

150

151

152

153

154

152 **Sir Herbert James Gunn, R.A.,**
P.R.P., R.S.W.
1893-1964
ZINNIAS
signed l.l.: *HJmes Gunn*
oil on canvas
61 by 45.5cm., 24 by 18in.

Provenance:
T & R Annan & Sons Ltd.

£3,000-5,000
€4,700-7,800

153 **Sir William MacTaggart, P.R.S.A.,**
R.S.W.
1903-1981
STILL LIFE
signed l.r.: *Mactaggart*; indistinctly
signed and inscribed with title on the
reverse
oil on board
61 by 38cm., 24 by 15in.

£3,000-5,000
€4,700-7,800

155

154 Sir William MacTaggart, P.R.S.A.,
R.S.W.
1903-1981
LILAC TIME; LANDSCAPE on verso
signed l.l.: *WMacTaggart*
oil on board
47 by 41cm., 18½ by 16¼in.

Provenance:
Aitken Dott & Son

£4,000-6,000
€6,300-9,400

155 James McIntosh Patrick, R.S.A.
1907-1998
EASDALE
signed and dated l.l.: *J MCINTOSH
PATRICK/30*
oil on canvas
71 by 91.5cm., 28 by 36in.

£20,000-30,000
€31,400-47,100

156 James McIntosh Patrick, R.S.A.
1907-1998
THE HARBOUR, AUCHMITHIE
signed l.l.: *MCINTOSH/PATRICK*;
inscribed with title on the stretcher;
signed and inscribed with title and
artists address on a label attached to
the frame
oil on canvas
71 by 91.5cm., 28 by 36in.

‡ £20,000-30,000
€31,400-47,100

156

157

158

159

157 James Fullarton
b.1946
LARGS MARINA
signed l.r.: *Fullarton*; signed and
inscribed with title on an label
attached to the reverse
oil on canvas board
40.5 by 51cm., 16 by 20in.

£2,000-3,000
€3,150-4,700

158 Donald McIntyre
b.1923
SITTING ON A ROCK, IONA
signed l.r.: *DMᶜ INTYRE*
oil on board
53 by 63.5cm., 21 by 25in.

£2,500-3,500
€3,900-5,500

159 William James Laidlaw Baillie
b.1923
HOTEL BEDROOM, GANGTOK
signed l.l.: *W.L.Baillie*
oil on canvas
102 by 127cm., 40 by 50in.

£2,000-3,000
€3,150-4,700

160 Winifred McKenzie
b.1905
STILL LIFE OF SPRING FLOWERS
signed l.r.: *Winifred McKenzie*
oil on canvas
61 by 45.5cm., 24 by 18in.

‡ £1,000-1,500
€1,550-2,350

161 Anne Davidson Muir, R.S.W.
1875-1951
POLYANTHUS
signed l.r.: *A.D.Muir*
oil on canvas
45.5 by 35.5cm., 18 by 14in.

£1,000-1,500
€1,550-2,350

162 Donald Bain
1904-1979
FROM MY WINDOW
signed and dated on the reverse: *D Bain/1943*
oil on canvas
63 by 76.5cm., 25 by 30in.

£2,000-3,000
€3,150-4,700

163 John Cunningham
b.1927
GARDENS - TOLEDO
signed l.r.: *JCunningham*; signed and inscribed with title on a gallery label attached to the backboard
gouache
34 by 49cm., 18½ by 19¼in.

Provenance:
James McClure & Sons

£1,200-1,800
€1,900-2,850

164 Donald Bain
1904-1979
BOAT HOUSES, JETTY, LOCH LOMOND
signed l.r.: *DBain*
oil on canvas board
48 by 60.5cm., 19 by 23¾in.

Provenance:
William Hardie Ltd

£2,000-3,000
€3,150-4,700

165 Lena M.Alexander
1899-1983
SUMMER FLOWERS
signed and indistinctly dated l.r.: *Lena Alexander*
coloured pastels
44 by 54cm., 17¼ by 21¼in.

£1,500-2,500
€2,350-3,900

162

163

164

166

167

169

166 David McClure, R.S.A., R.S.W.
1926-1998
NUMINOUS CHALICE
signed l.r.: *Mc Clure*; signed and
inscribed with title on the reverse
oil on canvas
63.5 by 76.5cm., 25 by 30in.

£5,000-8,000
€7,800-12,600

167 David McClure, R.S.A., R.S.W.
1926-1998
POSY OF FLOWERS
signed l.l.: *D.Mc Clure*
oil on board
38 by 28cm., 15 by 11in.

£4,000-6,000
€6,300-9,400

168 John Bellany
b.1942
FISH
signed on reverse: *J Bellany*
oil on canvas
46 by 51.5cm., 18 by 20¼in.

£1,000-1,500
€1,550-2,350

170

172

169 David McClure, R.S.A., R.S.W.
1926-1988
CRAIL
signed l.r.: *DM^c Clure*
oil on board
51 by 71cm., 20 by 28in.

£4,000-6,000
€6,300-9,400

170 John Bellany
b.1942
SWEET PROMISE
signed l.r.: *Bellany*, inscribed with
title along the lower edge
oil on canvas
76 by 61cm., 30 by 24in.

£2,000-3,000
€3,150-4,700

171 Sir Robin J.Philipson, R.A., R.S.W.
1916-1992
CARAVAN
signed l.r.: *R.Philipson*, bears title on
the reverse
watercolour with black ink
17½ by 17½cm., 7 by 7in.

Exhibited :
Edinburgh, Aitken Dott & Son,
Christmas Exhibition, 1963, no.2

£1,000-1,500
€1,550-2,350

172 Robert MacBryde
1913-1966
NATURE MORTE
signed l.l.: *M^{ac} Bryde*
oil on canvas
76 by 61cm., 30 by 24in.

£4,000-6,000
€6,300-9,400

173

174

173 **David McClure, R.S.A., R.S.W.**
1926-1998
FLOWERS
signed l.r.: *D.Mc Clure;* signed and
inscribed with title on the backboard
oil on canvas laid down on board
45.5 by 35.5cm., 18 by 14in.

£6,000-8,000
€9,400-12,600

174 **David McClure, R.S.A., R.S.W.**
1926-1998
FLOWERS IN MOONLIGHT
signed l.r.: *Mc Clure;* signed,
inscribed with title and dated *1967*
on the reverse
oil on canvas
45 by 56cm., 18 by 22in.,

£4,000-6,000
€6,300-9,400

175 **David McClure, R.S.A., R.S.W.**
1926-1998
FISHING BOAT AT SOURDON
signed l.l.: *D.Mc Clure*; signed and
inscribed with title on the reverse
oil on canvas laid down on board
25.5 by 35.5cm., 10 by 14in.

£2,000-3,000
€3,150-4,700

176 **David McClure, R.S.A., R.S.W.**
1926-1998
MALTESE FISHING BOATS
signed l.r.: *D.Mc Clure*; signed and
inscribed with title and artist's
address on the reverse
oil on canvas board
40.5 by 51cm., 16 by 20in.

£3,000-4,000
€4,700-6,300

177 **Peter Howson**
b.1958
GAME BOYS
signed l.l.: *HOWSON*
oil on canvas
61 by 91cm., 24 by 36in.

£2,000-3,000
€3,150-4,700

END OF SALE

175

176

177

INDEX

TOPOGRAPHICAL INDEX

GLOSSARY OF TERMS

Any statement as to authorship, attribution, origin, date, age, provenance and condition is a statement of opinion and is not to be taken as a statement of fact. Please read carefully the Conditions of Business, in particular Conditions 3 and 4.

1 **Giovanni Bellini**
In our opinion *a work by the artist*. (When the artist's forename(s) is not known, a series of asterisks, followed by the surname of the artist, whether preceded by an initial or not, indicates that in our opinion the work is by the artist named.

2 **attributed to Giovanni Bellini**
In our opinion *probably* a work by the artist but less certainty as to authorship is expressed than in the preceding category.

3 **studio of Giovanni Bellini**
In our opinion a work by an *unknown hand in the studio of the artist* which may or may not have been executed under the artist's direction.

4 **circle of Giovanni Bellini**
In our opinion a work by an as yet unidentified but distinct hand, closely associated with the named artist but not necessarily his pupil.

5 **style of............; follower of Giovanni Bellini**
In our opinion a work by a painter working *in the artist's style*, contemporary or nearly contemporary, but not necessarily his pupil.

6 **manner of Giovanni Bellini**
In our opinion a work in the style of the artist *and of a later date*.

7 **after Giovanni Bellini**
In our opinion a *copy* of a known work of the artist.

8 The term **signed** and/or **dated** and/or **inscribed** means that in our opinion the signature and/or date and/or inscription are from the hand of the artist.

9 The term **bears** a signature and/or **date** and/or **inscription** means that in our opinion the signature and/or date and/or inscription have been added by another hand.

10 Dimensions are given height before width.

11 Pictures are framed unless otherwise stated.

20th Century Decorative Arts & Design

AUCTION IN LONDON: 20TH APRIL 2001

Alexander Fisher, executed by the Royal School of Art Needlework, 1904

A 'Rose Tree' wall hanging designed for Farnhams Hall, Ware, Hertfordshire
Cream silk damask embroidered with crewel wools and silks, to be sold with two associated panels
Estimate: £10,000-15,000

Also to be sold from the same commission:
A set of 10 embroidered panels 'The Trossachs, Perthshire,' designed by Alexander Fisher, 1907
Estimate: £70,000-100,000

ENQUIRIES:
Lydia Cresswell-Jones
Philippe Garner
Carina Villinger
Tel: 020-7293 5379

CATALOGUES:
020 7293 6444
Fax: 020 7293 5909

SOTHEBY'S
34-35 New Bond Street
London W1A 2AA

www.sothebys.com

SOTHEBY'S
Founded 1744

John Houston, RSA
'She could have danced all night
across a crowded room,'
oil on canvas, signed,
65 by 76in., 165 by 193cm.
Offered by Corrymella Scott Gallery
Estimate: $10,000-15,000

THE SCOTTISH SALE

22nd March - 12th April 2001

Following the success of its first online special sale of
Scottish pictures, SOTHEBYS.COM will be holding a
second sale devoted to Scottish art. The sale will include
both traditional scenes of the 19th century, as well as a
section devoted to Modern and Contemporary Scottish
Art. The sale will coincide with Sotheby's annual Scottish
Sale at Hopetoun House

Enquiries: Suzy van den Berg Tel: 020 7293 6168
suzy.vandenberg@sothebys.com

AUCTIONS ONLINE

Special Auctions
Ancient and Ethnographic Art
Asian Art
Books & Manuscripts
Collectables & Memorabilia
Ceramics & Glass
Furniture & Decorative Arts
Jewellery
Paintings, Drawings, and Sculpture
Photographs
Prints
Silver & Vertu
Stamps, Coins & Medals
Watches & Clocks

SOTHEBYS.COM

257 YEARS OF EXPERIENCE, ONLINE

FINE ART · DECORATIVE ARTS & ANTIQUES · JEWELLERY & WATCHES · BOOKS · COLLECTABLES

Click on Current Special Auctions to find these extraordinary collections.
Sotheby's and its Associate Dealers bring thousands of lots in hundreds of
collecting categories together for auction only at SOTHEBYS.COM. Click on
"Subscribe" to receive advance invitations to bid on the objects that interest you.

Fine Scottish, Colourist & Sporting Pictures

AUCTION AT GLENEAGLES HOTEL, AUCHTERARDER, PERTHSHIRE, SCOTLAND: 5TH SEPTEMBER 2001

Richard Ansdell 1815-1885
The Auld Farmer's New Year's
Gift to His Auld Mare Maggie
Signed and dated l.r.:
R.Ansdell/1851
Oil on canvas
112 by 142cm. *44 by 56in.*
Sold at Gleneagles
30th August 2000 for £300,500

We are now accepting
consignments for our
forthcoming Scottish Sale.
Entries close 29th June 2001

ENQUIRIES:
London
Grant Ford
0207 293 5497
grant.ford@sothebys.com

Edinburgh
Harry Robertson
0131 226 7201
harry.robertson@sothebys.com

Glasgow
Anthony Weld Forester
0141 221 4817
anthony.weldforester@sothebys.com

SOTHEBY'S
34-35 New Bond Street
London W1A 2AA

www.sothebys.com

SOTHEBY'S
Founded 1744

GUIDE FOR PROSPECTIVE BUYERS

Buying at Auction

The following pages are designed to give you useful information on how to buy at auction. Sotheby's staff as listed at the front of this catalogue will be happy to assist you. It is important that you read the following information carefully.

Provenance

In certain circumstances, Sotheby's may print in the catalogue the history of ownership of a work of art if such information contributes to scholarship or is otherwise well known and assists in distinguishing the work of art. However, the identity of the seller or previous owners may not be disclosed for a variety of reasons. For example, such information may be excluded to accommodate a seller's request for confidentiality or because the identity of prior owners is unknown given the age of the work of art.

Buyer's Premium

With the exception of Wine, Coins and Books, the buyer's premium payable by the buyer of each lot is at a rate of 20% on the first £10,000 of the hammer price, 15% on the next £50,000 of the hammer price up to and including £60,000, and at a rate of 10% on the amount by which the hammer price exceeds £60,000.

VAT

Value Added Tax (VAT) may be payable on the hammer price and/or the buyer's premium. Buyer's premium may attract a charge in lieu of VAT. Please read carefully the "VAT INFORMATION FOR BUYERS" in this catalogue.

1. Before the Auction

Catalogue Subscriptions

If you would like to take out a catalogue subscription, please ring 020 7293 6410.

Pre-sale Estimates

Pre-sale estimates are intended as a guide for prospective buyers. Any bid between the high and low pre-sale estimates would, in our opinion, offer a chance of success. However, all lots can realise prices above or below the pre-sale estimates.

It is advisable to consult us nearer the time of sale as estimates can be subject to revision. The estimates printed in the auction catalogue do not include the buyer's premium or VAT.

Pre-sale Estimates in US Dollars and Euros

Although the sale is conducted in pounds sterling, the pre-sale estimates in some catalogues are also printed in US dollars and/or Euros. The rate of exchange is the rate at the time of production of this catalogue. Therefore, you should treat the estimates in US dollars or Euros as a guide only.

Condition of Lots

Prospective buyers are encouraged to inspect the property at the pre-sale exhibitions. Solely as a convenience, Sotheby's may provide condition reports. The absence of reference to the condition of a lot in the catalogue description does not imply that the lot is free from faults or imperfections. Please refer to Condition 4 of the Conditions of Business.

Electrical and Mechanical Goods

All electrical and mechanical goods are sold on the basis of their decorative value only and should not be assumed to be operative. It is essential that prior to any intended use, the electrical system is checked and approved by a qualified electrician.

2. Bidding in the Sale

Bidding at Auction

Bids may be executed in person by paddle during the auction, in writing prior to the sale or by telephone.

Auction speeds vary, but average between 50 and 120 lots per hour. The bidding steps are generally in increments of approximately 10% of the previous bid.

Please refer to Conditions 8, 9, 11, 12, 13, 14 and 15 of the Conditions of Business.

Bidding in Person

To bid in person, you will need to register for and collect a numbered paddle before the auction begins. Proof of identity will be required. If you have a Sotheby's Identification Card, it will facilitate the registration process. If you are an existing client and do not have a

card but would like one please contact the Bids department on 020 7293 5336.

Should you be the successful buyer of a lot, please ensure that your paddle can be seen by the auctioneer and that it is your number that is called out. Should there be any doubts as to price or buyer, please draw the auctioneer's attention to it immediately.

All lots sold will be invoiced to the name and address in which the paddle has been registered and cannot be transferred to other names and addresses.

Please do not mislay your paddle; in the event of loss, inform the Sales Clerk immediately. At the end of the sale, please return your paddle to the registration desk.

Absentee Bids

If you cannot attend the auction, we will be happy to execute written bids on your behalf. A bidding form can be found at the back of this catalogue. This service is free and confidential. Lots will always be bought as cheaply as is consistent with other bids, the reserves and Sotheby's commissions. In the event of identical bids, the earliest received will take precedence. Always indicate a "top limit" - the hammer price to which you would bid if you were attending the auction yourself. "Buy" and unlimited bids will not be accepted. Please refer to Condition 10(a) of the Conditions of Business.

Telephoned absentee bids must be confirmed before the sale by letter or fax. Fax number for bids only: 020 7293 6255.

To ensure a satisfactory service, please ensure that we receive your bids at least 24 hours before the sale.

Bidding by Telephone

If you cannot attend the auction, it is possible to bid on the telephone on lots with a minimum low estimate of £1,000. As the number of telephone lines is limited, it is necessary to make arrangements for this service 24 hours before the sale.

We also suggest that you leave a maximum bid which we can execute on your behalf in the event we are unable to reach you by telephone. Multi-lingual staff are available to execute bids for you. Please refer to Condition 10(b) of the Conditions of Business.

Employee Bidding

Sotheby's employees may bid only if the employee does not know the reserve and fully complies with Sotheby's internal rules governing employee bidding.

UN Embargo on trade with Iraq

The United Nations trade embargo prohibits us from accepting bids from any person in Iraq (including any body controlled by Iraqi residents or companies, wherever carrying on business), or from any other person where we have reasonable cause to believe (i) that the lot(s) will be supplied or delivered to or to the order of a person in Iraq or (ii) that the lot(s) will be used for the purposes of any business carried on in or operated from Iraq. Acceptance of bids by the auctioneer is subject to this prohibition.

For further details, please contact a member of the Specialist department or the Legal department PRIOR to bidding.

3. The Auction

Conditions of Business

The auction is governed by the Conditions of Business. These apply to all aspects of the relationship between Sotheby's and actual and prospective bidders and buyers. Anyone considering bidding in the auction should read them carefully. They may be amended by way of notices posted in the saleroom or by way of announcement made by the auctioneer.

Consecutive and Responsive Bidding

The auctioneer may open the bidding on any lot by placing a bid on behalf of the seller. The auctioneer may further bid on behalf of the seller, up to the amount of the reserve, by placing consecutive or responsive bids for a lot. Please refer to Condition 11 of the Conditions of Business.

4. After the Auction

Payment

Payment is due immediately after the sale and may be made by the following methods: **Sterling Cash, Sterling Banker's Draft, Sterling Travellers Cheques, Sterling Cheque, Wire Transfer in Sterling, Credit Card (Visa,** **Mastercard & Eurocard), Debit Card (Delta, Connect & Switch).**

Cheques and drafts should be made payable to **Sotheby's**. Although personal and company cheques drawn in Sterling on UK banks are accepted, you are advised that property will not be released until such cheques have cleared unless you have a pre-arranged **Cheque Acceptance Facility.** Forms to facilitate this are available from cashiers.
Bank transfers should be made to:
Barclays Bank plc
50 Pall Mall
London SW1A 1QA
Account name:
Sotheby's Client Receipts
Account No. 60163058
Sort Code: 20-67-59

Please include your name, Sotheby's account number and invoice number with your instructions to your bank.

Payment by Mastercard, Visa and Eurocard will be subject to a 1.5% administrative fee. Payments exceeding £20,000 can only be made by the card holder in person. For absentee payments below £20,000 please contact cashiers on 020 7293 5220.

The Conditions of Business require buyers to pay immediately for their purchases. However, in limited circumstances and with the seller's agreement, Sotheby's may offer buyers it deems credit worthy the option of paying for their purchases on an extended payment term basis. Generally credit terms must be arranged prior to the sale. In advance of determining whether to grant the extended payment terms, Sotheby's may require credit references and proof of identity and residence.

Collection

Lots will be released to you or your authorised representative when full and cleared payment has been received by Sotheby's and a release note has been produced by our Cashiers at New Bond Street, who are open Monday to Friday, 9 am to 5.30 pm.

Smaller items can be collected from the Packing Room at New Bond Street, large items will be sent to Sotheby's Kings House Warehouse.

If you are in any doubt about the location of your purchases, please contact the Sale Administrator prior to arranging collection. *Removal, interest, storage and handling charges will be levied on uncollected lots.* Please refer to Conditions 17 and 24 of the Conditions of Business.

Storage Charges

Storage and handling charges plus VAT will apply two weeks after the sale date for all purchased lots sent to Sotheby's Kings House at the following rates:
Handling Charge: £20 plus VAT per lot.
Storage Charge: £21 plus VAT per lot per week or part thereof.
Please refer to Condition 24 of the Conditions of Business.

Insurance

Buyers are reminded that lots are only insured **for a maximum of five (5) working days** after the day of the auction. Please refer to Condition 20 of the Conditions of Business.

Shipping

Sotheby's Shipping Logistics can advise buyers on exporting and shipping property. Our office is open between the hours of 9.00am and 5.30pm and you can contact the Shipping advisor on the number set out in the front of this catalogue.

Purchases will be despatched as soon as possible upon clearance from the Accounts department and receipt of your written despatch instructions and of any export licence or certificates that may be required. Despatch will be arranged at the buyer's expense. Sotheby's may receive a fee for its own account from the agent arranging the despatch. Estimates and information on all methods can be provided upon request and enquiries should be marked for the attention of Sotheby's Shipping Logistics and faxed to 020 7293 5952.

Transit insurance will be arranged unless otherwise specified in writing and will be at the buyer's expense. All shipments should be unpacked and checked on delivery and any discrepancies notified to the transit insurer or shipper immediately.

A form to provide shipping instructions is printed on the reverse of the bid slip in this catalogue or on the back of your buyers invoice.

Export

The export of any lot from the UK or import into any other country may be subject to one or more export or import licences being granted. It is the buyer's responsibility to obtain any relevant export or import licence. The denial of any licence required or delay in obtaining such licence cannot justify the cancellation of the sale or any delay in making payment of the total amount due.

Sotheby's, upon request and for an administrative fee, may apply for a licence to export your lot(s) outside the UK.

An *EU Licence* is necessary to export from the European Community cultural goods subject to the EU Regulation on the export of cultural property (EEC No. 3911/92, Official Journal No. L395 of 31/12/92.

A *UK Licence* is necessary to move from the UK to another Member State of the EU cultural goods valued at or above the relevant UK licence limit. A *UK Licence* may also be necessary to export outside the European Community cultural goods valued at or above the relevant UK licence limit but below the EU Licence limit.

The following is a selection of some of the categories and a summary of the limits above which either an EU or a UK licence may be required for items more than 50 years old:-

Paintings in oil or tempera	£119,000
Watercolours	£23,800
Prints, Drawings & Engravings	£11,900
British Historical Portraits	£6,000
Photographs	£6,000
Arms and Armour	£20,000
Textiles	£6,000
Printed Maps	£11,900
Books	£39,600
Any Other Objects	£39,600
Manuscripts/Archives/Scale Drawings	*
Archaeological items	*

(* a licence will be required in most instances, irrespective of value)

Export to Italy

Buyers intending to export their purchases to Italy under an Italian Temporary Cultural Import Licence are advised that the Italian authorities will require evidence of export from the UK. Please contact Sotheby's Shipping Representative or your own shipping agent prior to the export for more information.

Endangered Species

Items made of or incorporating plant or animal material, such as coral, crocodile, ivory, whalebone, tortoiseshell, etc., irrespective of age or value, may require a license or certificate prior to exportation and require additional licenses or certificates upon importation to any country outside the EU. Sotheby's suggests that buyers check with their own government regarding wildlife import requirements prior to placing a bid. Please note that the ability to obtain an export license or certificate does not ensure the ability to obtain an import license or certificate in another country, and vice versa. It is the buyer's responsibility to obtain any export or import licenses and/or certificates as well as any other required documentation (see Condition 22 of the Conditions of Business).

5. Additional Services

Financial Services

Sotheby's Financial Services makes loans to clients of Sotheby's. These include loans secured by property consigned for sale and loans secured by art collections which are not intended for sale. It is Sotheby's Financial Services' general policy to lend no more than 40% of the total of its low auction estimates for such property. It is also general policy that the minimum loan for consignor advances is £25,001 (in the US $50,000) and for secured loans is £500,000 (in the US $1,000,000). For further information please call Sotheby's Financial Services in New York at (1-212) 508 8061, or in London at (44) 20 7293 5273. This is not an offer or solicitation. The services described are subject to the laws and regulations of the jurisdiction in which any services may be provided.

Pre-sale auction estimates

Sotheby's will be pleased to give preliminary pre-sale auction estimates for your property. This service is free of charge and is available from Sotheby's experts in New Bond Street on week days between 9 am and 4.30 pm. We advise you to make an appointment with the relevant expert department. Upon request, we may also travel to your home to provide preliminary pre-sale auction estimates.

Valuations

The Valuation department provides written inventories and valuations throughout Europe for many purposes including insurance, probate and succession, asset management and tax planning. Valuations can be tailored to suit most needs. Fees are highly competitive. For further information please contact the Valuation department on 020 7293 5177/5082, fax 020 7293 5957.

Tax and Heritage Advice

Our Tax and Heritage department provides advice on the tax implications of sales and related legal and heritage issues. It can also assist in private treaty sales, on transfers in lieu of taxation, on the obtaining of conditional exemption from tax and on UK export issues. For further information, please contact the Tax and Heritage department on 020 7293 5082, fax 020 7293 5965.

SOTHEBY'S KINGS HOUSE

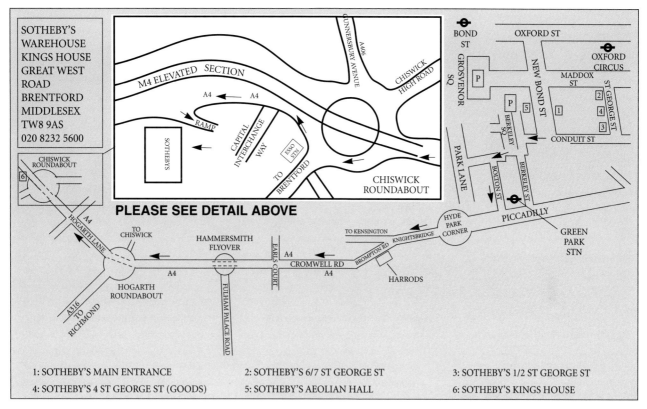

SOTHEBY'S
WAREHOUSE
KINGS HOUSE
GREAT WEST
ROAD
BRENTFORD
MIDDLESEX
TW8 9AS
020 8232 5600

PLEASE SEE DETAIL ABOVE

1: SOTHEBY'S MAIN ENTRANCE   2: SOTHEBY'S 6/7 ST GEORGE ST   3: SOTHEBY'S 1/2 ST GEORGE ST
4: SOTHEBY'S 4 ST GEORGE ST (GOODS)   5: SOTHEBY'S AEOLIAN HALL   6: SOTHEBY'S KINGS HOUSE

Consignors Information

Furniture, Longcase Clocks, large Works of Art, Carpets, Rugs, Tapestries and large Musical Instruments
Consignments mentioned in the above should be delivered to Sotheby's Kings House.
By appointment telephone 020 8232 5600.
Opening hours Monday to Friday 8.30am to 4.30pm, Saturdays 8.30am to 11.30am. Please arrive at least half an hour before closing.

Small items including Pictures, Ceramics, Silver and small Works of Art
Delivery in person between 9.00am and 4.30pm for all W1 locations.

Paintings and Books
1-2 St. George Street, London, W1A 2AA

Ceramics, Silver, Jewellery, small Works of Art and Oriental and Islamic Works of Art
6-7 St. George Street, London, W1A 2AA

Collectables, small Musical Instruments, Clocks and Watches, Wine, Stamps and Coins
Aeolian Hall, Bloomfield Place, London W1A 2AA

Delivery by Courier or Shipping Agent

When instructing a Courier or Shipper to deliver items to Sotheby's, address your property to the Arrivals Department, 1-2 St. George Street, London, W1A 2AA. Consignments sent by this method must be packed appropriately and clearly labelled with the owners name, address, telephone numbers, Sotheby's Client Account Number, (if known) and necessary licences from the country of export. Contact Sotheby's Shipping Department on 020 7293 5357 for further information.

To avoid delay ensure 3 days notice is given along with full consignment details.

Collection

Purchasers wishing to collect lots from Kings House must ensure that their payment has been cleared prior to collection and that a release note has been forwarded to the warehouse by the cashiers at Sotheby's New Bond Street. Buyers who have established credit arrangements with Sotheby's may collect purchases prior to payment, although a release note is still required from the cashiers as above. Please note that the cashiers department is not open on Saturdays. Lots will be released only if full payment has been received together with settlement of any removal, interest, handling and storage charges thereon. **Handling and storage**

charges plus VAT for all purchase lots sent to Sotheby's Kings House will apply two weeks after the sale date at the following rates:
Handling Charge: £20 plus VAT per lot
Storage Charge: £21 plus VAT per lot per week or part thereof.

Payments should be made to Sotheby's at Kings House.

Route Guidance

From Bond Street to Hyde Park Corner take the Knightsbridge Road leading into Brompton Road then the Cromwell Road. Over the Hammersmith Flyover onto the Great West Road. At the Hogarth Roundabout take the Hogarth Road to Chiswick. Follow the A4 route from slip road round the Chiswick Roundabout and take the second turning on the left. Follow the A4 past Capital Interchange on your left and take next left down the ramp signed Sotheby's. Kings House is situated adjacent to the DHL Building.

Kings House Warehouse

Paul Dennis and Salim Hasham
Telephone: 020 8232 5600
Fax: 020 8232 5625

01/01 G.KingsHouse

CONDITIONS OF BUSINESS

The conditions set out below and all other terms, conditions and notices set out in Sotheby's catalogues or announced by the auctioneer or posted in the sale room by way of notice (together 'the Conditions of Business') form the terms on which Sotheby's contracts, as auctioneer, with actual and prospective sellers and buyers. The Conditions of Business apply to all aspects of the relationship between you and us regarding the sale, purchase or holding by us of property. They also apply to you if you require inspection, appraisal or valuation of property. They are therefore very important and you should read them carefully. You agree that any future dealings which you may have with Sotheby's shall be on the Conditions of Business current at that particular time.

You should note that Sotheby's generally acts as agent for the seller. Any concluded contract of sale is made directly between the seller and the buyer.

Sotheby's is dependent on the seller for much of the relevant factual material pertaining to items offered for sale. Sotheby's cannot and does not undertake full due diligence on every item sold. Buyers therefore have a responsibility to carry out their own inspection and investigations to satisfy themselves as to the nature of the items which they are interested in buying. We specifically draw to the attention of all potential buyers Conditions 5 and 6 which limit the extent to which Sotheby's and the seller may be liable. We also specifically draw to the attention of all sellers Conditions 25 and 27 which set out the basis of the relationship between Sotheby's and the seller and limit the extent to which Sotheby's may be liable to the seller.

Actual and prospective buyers and sellers are bound by all Conditions of Business. However, for ease of reference, we have divided the Conditions set out below into sections. Section A explains certain terms that are used regularly throughout the Conditions, Section B sets out those Conditions which particularly relate to buyers, Section C sets out those Conditions which particularly relate to sellers, and Section D sets out those Conditions which relate to both buyers and sellers. Where possible in these Conditions of Business, Sotheby's is referred to as 'we', 'us' and 'our' and actual and prospective buyers and sellers are, as applicable, referred to as 'you' and 'your'.

A **Explanation and definition of certain terms used in the Conditions of Business**

1 **Definitions:** In these Conditions of Business, terms placed in inverted commas shall have the meaning set out below:

(a) 'buyer' means the person who makes the highest bid accepted by the auctioneer, or that person's disclosed principal;

(b) 'buyer's premium' means the commission on the 'hammer price' payable to 'Sotheby's' by a 'buyer' at the rates posted in the auction room at the time of the relevant sale, together with an amount in lieu of Value Added Tax ('VAT') if applicable;

(c) 'CITES' means Convention on International Trade in Endangered Species;

(d) 'expenses' in relation to the sale of any lot means 'Sotheby's' charges and expenses including but not limited to legal expenses, charges and expenses for insurance, catalogue and other reproductions and illustrations, any customs duties, advertising, packing or shipping costs, reproduction rights' fees, taxes, levies, costs of testing, searches or enquiries relating to any lot, or costs of collection from a defaulting 'buyer', plus an amount in lieu of VAT if applicable on illustration and insurance expenses;

(e) 'hammer price' means the price at which a lot is knocked down by the auctioneer to the 'buyer' or, in the case of a post-auction sale, the agreed price; in both instances excluding the 'buyer's premium', any applicable taxes and any 'expenses';

(f) 'low pre-sale estimate' means the low

estimate of 'Sotheby's' latest low and high pre-sale estimates of the value of the property, whether or not communicated to the 'seller';

(g) 'mid pre-sale estimate' means the average of 'Sotheby's' latest low and high pre-sale estimates of the value of the property, whether or not communicated to the 'seller';

(h) 'net sale proceeds' means the 'hammer price' of the lot sold to the extent received by 'Sotheby's' in cleared funds, less 'seller's commission' and 'expenses';

(i) 'seller' means the owner or the owner's agent or the person in possession of the property consigned. If there are multiple owners or agents or persons in possession, each shall assume, jointly and severally, all obligations, liabilities, representations, warranties and indemnities as set forth in these Conditions of Business;

(j) 'seller's commission' means the commission payable to 'Sotheby's' by a 'seller' at the rates applicable at the date of sale of the property or at the date of loss or damage to the property if applicable, together with an amount in lieu of VAT if applicable. The applicable 'seller's commission' rates are those set out in the 'Sotheby's' seller's commission rate cards which are available at Sotheby's offices at 34/35 New Bond Street, London W1A 2AA and the terms of which are incorporated in these Conditions of Business;

(k) 'Sotheby's' means Sotheby's, an unlimited company, company number 00874867;

(l) 'Sotheby's affiliated company' means Sotheby's Holdings, Inc. and any company (other than Sotheby's) being a subsidiary of Sotheby's Holdings, Inc. for the time being within the meaning of Section 736 of the Companies Act 1985;

(m) 'total amount due' means the 'hammer price' in respect of the lot sold, together with the 'buyer's premium', and any charges, fees, interest, taxes and 'expenses' due from a 'buyer' or defaulting 'buyer'.

B **Conditions mainly concerning buyers**

2 **Sotheby's capacity:** 'Sotheby's' sells as agent for the 'seller' except where it wholly or partly owns any lot as principal. 'Sotheby's' may have a legal or equitable interest in, or have made a financial commitment in respect of, the lot as secured creditor or otherwise. Where

'Sotheby's' sells as agent, any sale will result in a contract made directly between the 'seller' and the 'buyer'.

Sotheby's obligations to buyers

3 *Our guarantee to you in respect of counterfeit lots:* If we sell a lot which subsequently proves to be a counterfeit, we shall set aside the sale and refund to you any amount paid by you to us in connection with the lot in the currency of the original sale. This, however, shall only be available on condition that, no later than five (5) years after the date of the sale, you:
(i) notify us in writing of the number of the lot, the date of the auction at which it was purchased and the reasons why you consider the lot to be counterfeit, within three (3) months of any information causing you to question the authenticity or attribution of the lot coming to your attention;
(ii) are able to transfer good title to us free from any third party claims arising after the date of the sale to you; and
(iii) return the lot to us in the same condition as at the date of sale, provided that, in any event, no refund will be available if either:
(a) the catalogue description at the date of the sale was in accordance with the generally accepted opinions of scholars and experts at that time or the catalogue description indicated that there was a conflict of such opinions; or
(b) the only method of establishing that the lot was a counterfeit at the date of publication of the catalogue was by means of processes which either were not generally accepted for use until after the publication of the catalogue or else were unreasonably expensive or impractical or likely to have caused damage to the lot or likely, in our reasonable opinion, to have caused loss of value to the lot.
An item shall be considered counterfeit where, in our reasonable opinion, it is a deliberate modern forgery, i.e. an imitation created since 1870 with the intention of deceiving as to authorship, origin, date, age, period, culture or source (where the correct description of such matters is not reflected by the description in the catalogue) and which, at the date of sale, had a value materially less than it would have had if the item had been in accordance

with the description in the catalogue. No lot shall be considered a counterfeit by reason only of any damage and/or restoration and/or modification work of any kind (including repainting or overpainting).

It is our general policy, and we shall have the right to request the 'buyer' to obtain at the 'buyer's' cost the reports of two independent and recognised experts in the field, mutually acceptable to the 'buyer' and to us, setting out the reasons why the lot in question is considered to be counterfeit and 'Sotheby's' agrees that it will give due consideration to any such expert reports. However, 'Sotheby's' reserves the right to seek additional independent advice itself in making its final determination as to whether the lot is a counterfeit and we shall not be bound by any expert report produced by the 'buyer'. If we agree with the 'buyer' that the lot is a counterfeit, we shall refund to 'the buyer' the costs of obtaining two independent expert reports incurred by the 'buyer' provided that (i) such costs were approved by us in advance of obtaining such reports, and (ii) the 'buyer' could not reasonably have obtained independent opinions prior to the sale.

The benefit of this guarantee is not capable of being transferred and is solely for the benefit of the 'buyer'.

Buyer's obligation to inspect

4 *Examination of goods:* Goods auctioned are usually of some age. All goods are sold with all faults and imperfections and errors of description. Illustrations in catalogues are for identification only. You should also note that we have not tested any electrical or mechanical goods prior to the sale (whether in respect of their ability to function, their safety of operation or otherwise) and you are solely responsible for testing such goods before using them.

Accordingly, as regards any lot in which you are interested, you undertake:
(i) to inspect and satisfy yourself prior to the sale as to the condition and description of the lot;
(ii) to rely on your own judgment as to whether the lot accords with its description;
(iii) to seek any independent expert advice

reasonable (in the light of your particular expertise and the value of the lot) to satisfy yourself as to authorship, attribution, authenticity, genuineness, origin, date, age, provenance or condition of the lot; and
(iv) not to rely on any illustration in any catalogue.

To assist you, we may refer in a catalogue to particular faults or imperfections, but any such guidance which we provide does not purport to be exhaustive. You will be deemed to have knowledge of all matters which you could reasonably have been expected to find out given your particular expertise and the exercise by you of reasonable due diligence.

Sotheby's liability to buyers

5 *Exclusion of liability:* Apart from the guarantee in Condition 3 given by 'Sotheby's' to the 'buyer' and your rights in relation to the conduct of auctions as set out in Condition 11:
(i) 'Sotheby's' gives no guarantees or warranties to the 'buyer' and any implied warranties or conditions are excluded (save in so far as such obligations cannot be excluded by statute);
(ii) in particular, any representations, written or oral and including those in any catalogue, report, commentary or valuation, in relation to any aspect or quality of any lot, including price or value, (a) are statements of opinion only and (b) may be revised prior to the lot being offered for sale (including whilst the lot is on public view); and
(iii) none of 'Sotheby's', any 'Sotheby's' affiliated company', or any agent, employee or director thereof shall be liable for any errors or omissions in any such representations.

6 *Limitation on claims by buyers:* Without prejudice to Conditions 3 and 5 above, and save insofar as it relates to any liability which we may have for personal injury or death, any claim against 'Sotheby's' by the 'buyer' shall be limited to the 'hammer price' and the 'buyer's premium' actually paid by the 'buyer' to 'Sotheby's' with regard to that lot.

Seller's liability to buyers

7 *Seller's obligations to buyers:* The 'seller's'

obligations to you are limited to the same extent as our obligations to you. Any express or implied conditions or warranties are excluded save insofar as it is not possible to exclude obligations implied by statute. In addition, we reserve the right to agree variations to the 'seller's' warranties with the 'seller'.

At the sale

8   *Rights of participation at auction:* We have the right, at our absolute discretion, to refuse to allow any person to participate in our auctions and to refuse admission to our premises to any person.

9   *Bidding as principal:* If you make a bid at auction, you do so as principal and will be held personally and solely liable for that bid unless we have previously agreed with you in writing that you do so on behalf of an identified third party who is acceptable to us. In circumstances where we have so agreed, both you and the third party will be jointly and severally liable for all obligations arising from the bid and the third party shall be bound by the Conditions of Business by your bidding as his agent in the same way as if he were bidding personally.

10   *Commission and telephone bids:* Although your interests are likely to be best served if you attend auctions in person, you may bid by telephone or by leaving a commission bid as set forth below.
(a)   *Commission bids:* We will seek to carry out any instructions to bid at an auction on your behalf which we receive from you sufficiently in advance of the sale and which we consider, in our discretion, to be sufficiently clear and complete. If we receive commission bids on a particular lot for identical amounts, and at auction these bids are the highest bids for the lot, it will be sold to the person whose bid was received first by us. However, our obligation in relation to commission bids is undertaken subject to our other commitments at the time of sale and the conduct of the sale may be such that we are unable to bid as requested. We cannot accept liability for failure to make a commission bid for any reason. You should therefore attend personally or send an agent to the auction if you wish to be certain of bidding.
(b)   *Telephone bids:* We may be prepared to allow you to bid by telephone but, in such circumstances, we reserve the right to require you to confirm relevant details in writing before we agree to do so. We are not responsible for the failure of any telephone bid for any reason. We reserve the right to record telephone bids.

11   *Conduct of the auction:* The auctioneer will commence and advance the bidding in levels that he considers appropriate in the light of the value of the lot under auction and of competing bids. The auctioneer is entitled to make consecutive bids or make bids in response to other bids on behalf of the 'seller' up to the reserve placed on the lot, although the auctioneer will not indicate during the auction that he is making such bids on behalf of the 'seller'. The 'buyer' acknowledges the rights of the auctioneer and the 'seller' set out in this Condition and waives any claim that he might have in this connection against 'Sotheby's' or the 'seller'.

12   *Sale of a lot:* The person who makes the highest bid accepted by the auctioneer (or that person's disclosed principal, if applicable) shall be the 'buyer'. The striking of the auctioneer's hammer marks the acceptance of the highest bid and identifies the 'hammer price' at which the lot is knocked down by the auctioneer to the 'buyer'. The striking of the auctioneer's hammer also marks the conclusion of a contract of sale between the 'seller' and the 'buyer'.

13   *Auctioneer's discretion:* Notwithstanding Conditions 11 and 12 above, the auctioneer has absolute discretion at any time during the course of the auction to:
(i)   withdraw any lot;
(ii)   re-offer a lot for sale if the auctioneer reasonably believes that there is an error or dispute; and/or
(iii)   take such other action as he reasonably thinks fit in the circumstances.

14   *Currency converter:* Auctions are conducted in pounds sterling. Where a currency converter is operated, it is for your convenience only. Errors may occur in the currency converter and you should not rely on it as a substitute for the sterling bidding.

15   *Video images:* At some auctions, there will be a video screen in operation for the convenience of both 'buyers' and 'sellers'. Errors may occur in the operation of the video screen. We cannot accept responsibility either for the quality of the image reproduced on the video screen, nor for the correspondence of the screen image to the original.

After the sale

16   *Payment:* Immediately after the conclusion of the relevant session of the auction in which the lot was sold, you shall pay us, in pounds sterling, the 'total amount due (including 'buyer's premium'). Payment will not be deemed to have been made until we are in receipt of cash or cleared funds.

17   *Collection of purchases:* You shall collect the purchased lot, at your expense, no later than five working days after the day of the sale. Unless we exercise our discretion to do so, and without prejudice to Condition 23(g) below, the lot shall not be released to you before receipt by us of the 'total amount due'.

18   *Passing of title:* You shall always remain liable for the 'total amount due' and you shall not acquire title to the lot sold until you have made payment in full of the 'total amount due' in respect of that lot and 'Sotheby's' has applied such payment to the lot (even if, without prejudice to Condition 17, we exercise our discretion to release it to you). Other than where we have agreed with you to the contrary, and subject to Condition 23(d) below, any monies received from you shall be applied in order of the oldest debt owed by you to 'Sotheby's' or the oldest purchase made by you at 'Sotheby's' or any 'Sotheby's affiliated company' having regard to the date of sale and the number of the lot.

19   *Proceeds of on-sale:* In circumstances where you on-sell the lot or any part of the lot before making payment in full to us of the 'total amount due', you agree to:
(i)   hold on trust for us the proceeds of that sale to the extent that they are equal to the 'total amount due' less any amounts from time

to time paid to us applied to that lot; and

(ii) keep the amount that you hold on trust for 'Sotheby's' in respect of any lot in a separate bank account.

20 *Transfer of risk:* Any lot purchased is entirely at your risk from the earlier of:

(i) the time you collect the lot purchased; or

(ii) the time that you pay to us the 'total amount due' for the lot; or

(iii) five (5) working days after the day of the sale.

You shall be solely responsible for insuring the lot purchased from the time risk passes to you.

You will be compensated for any loss or damage to the lot which occurs after sale but prior to the time risk passes to you. The maximum amount of compensation shall be the 'hammer price' of the lot plus the 'buyer's premium' received by 'Sotheby's', and shall exclude any indirect or consequential loss or damage. However, we will not, in any circumstances, be liable for any loss or damage caused to frames or to glass which is covering prints, paintings or other works unless the frame or glass is, in itself, the object sold at auction. Nor will we be liable for loss or damage caused by any of the events set out in Condition 31 below.

21 *Packing and handling:* The packing and handling of lots is entirely at your risk and expense and we shall not, in any circumstances, be responsible for any acts or omissions of the packers or shippers.

22 *Export:* The export of any lot from the United Kingdom or import into any other country may be subject to one or more export or import licences being granted. It is the 'buyer's' responsibility to obtain any relevant export or import licence. Lots purchased shall be paid for in accordance with Condition 16 and the denial of any export or import licence required or any delay in the obtaining of such licence shall not justify the rescission or cancellation of the sale by you or any delay by you in making payment of the 'total amount due' for the lot.

23 *Remedies for non-payment:* If the 'total amount due' is not paid on any lot in accordance with Condition 16, we shall, in

our discretion and without prejudice to any other rights which we and the 'seller' may have, be entitled, both for ourselves and as agent for the 'seller', to exercise any one or more of the following rights or remedies:

(a) commence proceedings against you for damages for breach of contract;

(b) cancel the sale of the lot;

(c) apply any payments made by you to us or any 'Sotheby's affiliated company' as part of the 'total amount due' or otherwise towards any costs or 'expenses' incurred in connection with the sale of the lot;

(d) apply any payments made by you to us or any 'Sotheby's affiliated company' as part of the 'total amount due' or otherwise towards any other debts owed by you to us or any other 'Sotheby's affiliated company' in respect of any other transaction;

(e) arrange and carry out a re-sale of the lot by public auction or private sale in mitigation of the debt owed by you to us. You and the 'seller' consent to and authorise us to arrange and carry out such re-sale on the Conditions of Business applicable at the time of such re-sale and agree that the level of the reserve and the estimates relevant to such re-sale shall be set at our sole discretion. The 'net sale proceeds' will be applied in reduction of your debt. If a re-sale should result in a lower price than the original 'hammer price' obtained, we and the 'seller' shall be entitled to claim the balance from you together with any costs incurred in connection with your failure to make payment. If the re-sale should result in a higher price than the original 'hammer price' obtained, the surplus shall be paid to the 'seller'. In such case, you waive any claim which you may have to title to the lot and agree that any re-sale price shall be deemed commercially reasonable;

(f) set off any amounts owed by us or any 'Sotheby's affiliated company' to you against any amounts which you owe to us or any 'Sotheby's affiliated company', whether as the result of any proceeds of sale or otherwise;

(g) exercise a lien over any of your property which is in our possession or in possession of any 'Sotheby's affiliated company' for any reason until payment of all outstanding amounts due to us have been made in full. We shall notify you of any lien being exercised

and the amount outstanding. If the amount outstanding then remains unpaid for fourteen days following such notice, we shall be entitled to arrange and carry out the sale of any such property in accordance with (e) above;

(h) charge you the 'seller's' and our reasonable legal and administrative costs incurred;

(i) charge you interest at a rate not exceeding 6% (six per cent) per annum above the base lending rate quoted by Barclays Bank plc from time to time on the 'total amount due' to the extent that it remains unpaid for more than five (5) working days after the date of the auction;

(j) insure, remove and store the lot either at our premises or elsewhere at your sole risk and expense;

(k) reject any bids made by or on your behalf at any future auction or require you to make a deposit with us before accepting any such bids.

24 *Remedies for failure to collect purchases:* If you do not collect a purchased lot within five working days after the sale, we may arrange storage of the lot at your risk and expense. This shall apply whether or not you have made payment of the 'total amount due'. We shall release the purchased lot only after you have made payment in full of all storage, removal, insurance and any other costs incurred, together with payment of all other amounts due to us including, if applicable, the 'total amount due'. We shall, in our absolute discretion, also be entitled to exercise any of the rights or remedies listed in Condition 23 (a), (c), (e), (f), (g) and (h) above, provided that we shall not exercise our right under Condition 23 (e) above for a period of six months following the relevant sale. In the event that we exercise our rights under Condition 23 (e) above, we undertake to hold to your order the 'net sale proceeds' received by us in cleared funds less all storage, removal, insurance and any other costs or taxes incurred.

C *Conditions mainly concerning Sellers*

25 *Seller's warranties:* This Condition governs your relationship with both the 'buyer' and

ourselves. If we or the buyer consider any of the warranties listed below to be breached in any way, either we or the 'buyer' may take legal action against you. You agree to indemnify 'Sotheby's' and any 'Sotheby's affiliated company', their respective servants, directors, officers and employees and the 'buyer' against any loss or damage resulting from any breach or alleged breach of any of your representations or warranties, or other terms set forth in these Conditions of Business. Where we reasonably believe that any breach of such representation or warranty has occurred, you authorise 'Sotheby's' in its sole discretion, to rescind the sale.

You warrant to us and to the 'buyer' that at all relevant times (including but not limited to the time of the consignment of the property and the time of the sale):

(a) you are the true owner of the property, or are properly authorised to sell the property by the true owner;

(b) you are able to and shall, in accordance with these Conditions of Business, transfer possession to the 'buyer' and good and marketable title to the property free from any third party rights or claims or potential claims including, without limitation, any claims which may be made by governments or governmental agencies;

(c) you have provided us with all information concerning the provenance of the property and have notified us in writing of any concerns expressed by third parties in relation to the ownership, condition, authenticity, attribution, or export or import of the lot;

(d) you are unaware of any matter or allegation which would render any description given by us in relation to the lot inaccurate or misleading;

(e) where the property has been moved to the European Union from a country that is not a member of the European Union, the property has been lawfully imported into the European Union; the property has been lawfully and permanently exported as required by the laws of any country in which it was located; required declarations upon the export and import of the property have been properly made; any duties and taxes on the export and import of the property have been paid;

(f) you have or will pay any and all taxes and/or duties that may be due on the 'net sale proceeds' of the property and you have notified us in writing of any or all taxes and for duties that are payable by us on your behalf in any country other than the country of the sale;

(g) unless you advise us in writing to the contrary at the time you deliver the property to us, there are no restrictions, copyright or otherwise, relating to the property (other than those imposed by law) and no restrictions on our rights to reproduce photographs or other images of the property; and

(h) unless you advise us in writing to the contrary at the time you deliver the property to us, any electrical or mechanical goods (or any electrical or mechanical parts of lots being offered for sale) are in a safe operating condition if reasonably used for the purpose for which they were designed and are free from any defect not obvious on external inspection which could prove dangerous to human life or health.

Before the sale

26 *Preparation for sale:* You agree that we shall have sole and absolute discretion as to:

(i) the way in which property may be combined or divided into lots for sale;

(ii) the way in which lots are included in the sale;

(iii) the way in which any lot is described and illustrated in the catalogue or any condition report;

(iv) the date and place of the auction(s); and

(v) the manner in which any sale is conducted.

We reserve the right to consult with and rely on any outside experts, consultants or restorers of our choice in relation to the property and to carry out such other inquiries or tests in relation to the property either before or after the sale as we may, in our absolute discretion, deem appropriate. This is, however, a matter for our discretion and we are under no duty to carry out such consultation, inquiries or tests.

27 (a) *Estimates:* Any estimate given by us, whether written or oral, is a matter of opinion only and is intended only as a guide. An estimate shall not be relied upon as a prediction of the anticipated selling price. Any estimate given (whether written or oral and whether in a catalogue, receipt, letter or otherwise) may, in our absolute discretion, be revised from time to time.

(b) *Exclusion of liability:* Any representations, written or oral and including those in any catalogue, report, commentary or valuation in relation to any aspect or quality of any lot, including price or value (a) are statements of opinion only and (b) may be revised prior to the lot being offered for sale (including whilst the lot is on public view). Neither 'Sotheby's', any 'Sotheby's affiliated company', nor any agent employee or director thereof shall be liable for any errors or omissions in any such representations.

(c) *Limitations on claims by seller:* Any claim by the 'seller' (excluding any claim covered by Condition 31) shall, in any event, be limited to the 'net sale proceeds' in respect of that lot.

28 *Withdrawal of lots by you:* If you choose to withdraw property from the sale after the earlier of (i) your written agreement to sell the property with us and (ii) 12 weeks before the date of the auction of the property, you will be liable to pay to us a withdrawal fee calculated in accordance with Condition 30 below. If you withdraw property before that time, no withdrawal fee shall be payable.

29 *Withdrawal of lots by us:* We may withdraw a lot from sale without any liability if (i) we reasonably believe that there is any doubt as to its authenticity or attribution or (ii) it is established or alleged that any of the seller's representations or warranties set out in Condition 25 above are inaccurate in any way or (iii) you breach any provisions of the Conditions of Business in any material respect or (iv) the lot contains any endangered species for which a 'CITES' sale exemption is required and the sale exemption has not been granted by the day preceding the first day of the viewing of the sale or (v) we consider the lot to be of insufficient sale value or (vi) the lot suffers from loss or damage so that it is not in the state in which it was when we agreed to sell it or (vii) the auction at which it was proposed to sell the lot is postponed for any

reason.

If we become aware of a competing title claim to, or lien over, a lot consigned by you, we shall not release the lot to you until the title claim or lien, as applicable, has been finally resolved to our satisfaction.

30 *Withdrawal fee:* If the property is withdrawn because the circumstances described in any of (i), (iv), (v), (vi) or (vii) of Condition 29 above occurs, then you shall not be charged a withdrawal fee and the property shall be returned to you at your expense provided that there is no adverse title claim on the property. If, however, the property is withdrawn for any other reason, you shall pay us a withdrawal fee together with any 'expenses'. The withdrawal fee shall be equal to the sum of the 'seller's commission' and the 'buyer's premium' and shall be calculated as if the withdrawn property had sold at the 'mid pre-sale estimate'. The rate of 'seller's commission' shall be the rate applicable at the time of consignment of the withdrawn lot. We shall not be obliged to withdraw any property from sale or to return it to you unless you have paid us the withdrawal fee.

31 *Risk of loss or damage - risk borne by us:* Unless otherwise agreed with us in writing at the time of delivery of the lot to us, we will, at your expense, and on the terms set out in this Condition 31, bear the risk of loss or damage in any lot from the time we receive such property until (i) risk passes to the 'buyer' of the lot following sale of the lot, or (ii) 60 days after the relevant auction, if the lot is unsold or (iii) 6 months after the lot has been delivered to us, if it remains in our possession and has not been consigned for sale by then.

We shall charge you, and you agree to pay, a sum in respect of the risk borne by us at a rate which shall be equal to one per cent (1%) of:
(i)   the 'hammer price', if the lot is sold; or
(ii) the 'reserve price', if the lot is unsold; or
(iii) the 'mid pre-sale estimate', if the lot is not offered for sale for any reason; or
(iv) if there is no 'mid pre-sale estimate' then a reasonable estimate of the auction value of the lot at the date at which it was delivered to us.

Where (i) above applies, you agree that

we may deduct such a sum from the 'hammer price' of the lot.

If any loss or damage should occur to the property whilst the risk in it is borne by us, we shall not be liable to pay you any more than the amount set out in (i)-(iv) above, as applicable, less 'seller's commission' plus 'expenses' and any applicable VAT on each of the 'seller's commission' and 'expenses'. If the property is partially damaged or partially lost and has depreciated in value, in our opinion, by less than 50%, we shall either (i) pay you the amount of depreciation and the property will be offered for sale or returned to you, or (ii) pay you for the property as set forth in the preceding sentence, and you will no longer own the property.

We will not be liable for any loss or damage caused to frames or to glass covering prints, paintings or other work. Nor will we be liable for loss or damage caused by:
(i)   any third party whom we have instructed to deal with the property with your consent;
(ii) changes in humidity or temperature;
(iii) normal wear and tear, gradual deterioration or inherent vice or defect;
(iv) errors in processing;
(v) war, weapons of war employing atomic fission, or radioactive contamination.

32 *Risk of loss or damage: - cover arranged by you:* If you do not wish us to bear the risk of loss or damage cover in any lot delivered to us, you must agree this with us in writing at that time. In the event that you agree this with us, you will maintain insurance cover for the lot until the 'buyer' has made payment for the lot in full. In such circumstances, you agree to:
(i)   provide us with a copy of a certificate of insurance for the lot;
(ii) procure a waiver of subrogation by your insurer of all rights and claims which they may have against us in connection with loss or damage, such waiver of subrogation in a form satisfactory to us, and to provide us with a copy of such waiver;
(iii) indemnify us against any claim for loss, damage or costs in respect of the lot, however that claim may arise;
(iv) notify your insurer of the terms of the indemnity set out in (iii) above;
(v) reimburse us on demand for all

payments, costs or 'expenses', including legal fees, which we incur as a result of any claim. Any payment which we make under this Condition shall be binding upon you and shall be accepted by you as being conclusive evidence that we were required to make such payment, even where no legal liability has been proved; and
(vi) waive all rights and claims which you may have against us in connection with such loss or damage, other than in circumstances where the loss or damage was caused by our wilful misconduct.

If you fail to comply with sub paragraphs (i) and (ii) above within 10 days of delivery of any lot to us, we shall bear the risk of loss or damage in the lot in accordance with the terms of Condition 31 above. We shall bear such risk of loss or damage from the start of the 11th day following the day of delivery of the lot to us. If any loss or damage should occur to the lot after that time, our liability to you shall be limited to the excess, if any, of (a) the relevant amount set out in (i)-(iv) of Condition 31 above, over (b) any amount payable to you for such loss or damage under the insurance policy you agreed to maintain for the lot under this Condition plus any deductible applicable thereunder.

33 *Reconsignment:* We may, at our discretion, decide to reconsign any lot so that it shall be offered for sale at public auction by another 'Sotheby's affiliated company'. We shall notify you in writing if we decide to do this and, unless you object in writing within ten (10) days of such notice, you shall be treated as consenting to such reconsignment. In those circumstances, any sale shall be conducted under the Conditions of Business in the relevant sale catalogue, save only that, as between you and us, these Conditions of Business shall continue to apply and shall prevail in the event of any conflict. Any proceeds of sale shall be remitted to you in the currency in which the auction is conducted and all local taxes shall apply.

At the sale

34 *Reserves:* Unless otherwise agreed in writing, each lot will be offered for sale subject to a reserve of seventy five per cent (75%) of the

low pre-sale estimate agreed with you. If you and 'Sotheby's' are unable to agree on a low pre-sale estimate, the reserve shall be seventy five per cent (75%) of our 'low pre-sale estimate'.

No reserve will exceed the final 'low pre-sale estimate' announced or published by us, other than in circumstances where the reserve agreed is in a currency other than pounds sterling and the exchange rates fluctuate between the time the reserve is agreed and the day of the auction. In those circumstances, if we are unable to agree a revised reserve with you, the reserve shall be an amount equal to the pounds sterling equivalent based on the closing exchange rate available on the business day immediately preceding the auction.

We shall in no circumstances be liable if bids are not received at the level of the reserve but shall be entitled, in our discretion, to sell the lot below the reserve. If we do so, we shall pay you the sale proceeds which you would have received if the lot had sold at the reserve. If a lot fails to sell, the auctioneer will announce that the lot is unsold.

35 *Bidding at the sale:* You may not bid for your own property. Although we shall be entitled to bid on your behalf up to the amount of the reserve, you shall not instruct or permit any other person to bid for the property on your behalf. If you should bid on your own behalf (or instruct someone else to do so), we may treat you as the successful bidder. In those circumstances, you shall not be entitled to the benefit of Conditions 3 and 34 above and you shall pay to us a sum representing the total of the 'seller's commission', the 'buyer's premium' and all 'expenses' which we have incurred in connection with the sale of the lot. We shall be entitled to exercise a lien over the lot until payment of that sum has been made by you in full.

After the sale

36 *Payment to be made by you to us:* Following the sale, you will be liable to pay us the following sums:
 (i) the 'seller's commission'; and
 (ii) 'expenses'.
 We shall be entitled to deduct each of

these items from monies received from the 'buyer'. You authorise Sotheby's to charge the buyer and retain the 'buyer's premium'.

37 *Payment of net sale proceeds to you:* Unless we have been notified by the 'buyer' of his intention to rescind the sale on the basis that the lot is a counterfeit, we shall send to you on the thirty fifth day after the final day of the auction, the 'net sale proceeds' received from the 'buyer' in cleared funds, less any other amount you owe us or any 'Sotheby's affiliated company'. You should note that the 'net sale proceeds' payable to you are derived from the actual proceeds of sale received by us from the 'buyer'. Where the 'buyer' makes payment more than 30 days after the final day of the relevant sale, we shall send you the 'net sale proceeds' less any other amount you owe us or any 'Sotheby's affiliated company' within 5 working days of receipt of cleared funds. We reserve the right to release a lot to the 'buyer' before we receive the 'total amount due' for the lot. If we choose to do so, we shall remit to you the 'net sale proceeds' of the lot on the thirty fifth day after the final day of the auction.

38 *Rescission:* Where we are satisfied that the lot is a counterfeit, we shall rescind the sale and notify you of such rescission. We shall, in our absolute discretion, be entitled to dispense with the requirements of Condition 3 in determining whether or not a particular lot is a counterfeit. Within ten (10) days of receipt of the notice advising you of the rescission of sale, you will return to us any 'net sale proceeds' previously paid by us to you in connection with the lot and shall reimburse us for any 'expenses' incurred in connection with the rescinded sale. On receipt of such funds, we shall return the lot to you. We shall be entitled to the 'net sale proceeds' of the lot if, for reasons beyond our control, we cannot return the lot to you.

39 *Non-payment by the buyer:* We are under no obligation to enforce payment by any 'buyer' nor to undertake legal proceedings to recover such payment. You agree to inform us of any action which you choose to take against the 'buyer' to enforce payment of the amount due to you.

We have absolute discretion to take and enforce any of the remedies set out in Condition 23 above including the right to cancel the sale and return the property to you. On your request, we will inform you of any action being taken against the 'buyer' and shall give consideration to any views which you may express to us on the appropriate course of action to take to recover the amount due.

We shall be entitled to charge the 'buyer' interest for late payment in accordance with Condition 23(i) above and you authorise us to retain such interest for our own account.

If the 'buyer' fails to pay the 'total amount due' but we agree to remit to you an amount equal to the 'net sale proceeds', ownership of the relevant lot shall pass to us. For the avoidance of doubt, we shall have the benefit of all of your representations, warranties and indemnities set out in these Conditions of Business.

40 *Post-auction sales:* If any lot fails to sell at auction, we shall be entitled for a period of forty (40) days following the auction to sell the lot. Unless you agree to the contrary, any post-auction sale shall only be concluded for a price that will result in a payment to you of not less than the 'net sale proceeds' to which you would have been entitled had the lot been sold at the reserve price. If a post-auction sale is agreed, your obligations to us and the 'buyer' with respect to such lot are the same as if the lot had been sold at auction. Any reference in the Conditions of Business to the date of the auction shall be treated as being a reference to the date of the post-auction sale.

41 *Unsold lot:* We will send you a notice to the address given on the relevant property receipt form if any lot fails to sell at auction. If such lot has not been sold privately pursuant to Condition 40 above, you shall either reconsign the lot to us for re-sale or, alternatively, collect the lot from us. If you decide to collect the lot, we reserve the right to charge you a reduced commission amounting to fifty per cent (50%) of the 'seller's commission', plus 'expenses'. The 'seller's commission' shall in these circumstances be calculated as if the lot had

sold at the reserve price. The rate of 'seller's commission' shall be the rate applicable at the date of the auction.

If you fail either to reconsign or collect the lot as set out above within sixty (60) days of the auction, we shall, in our sole discretion, be entitled to:

(i) store the lot at an independent storage facility at your risk and expense; or

(ii) re-offer the lot for sale at public auction with a reserve no less than fifty per cent (50%) of the original reserve.

In the event of such re-sale, we shall be entitled to deduct from the 'hammer price' the reduced commission in respect of the initial sale plus 'expenses' together with the 'seller's commission' on the re-sale plus 'expenses'. We reserve the right to charge you our reasonable legal and administrative costs incurred.

Any re-sale shall be conducted under the Conditions of Business printed in the sale catalogue of the relevant sale, save only that, as between you and us, these Conditions of Business shall continue to apply and shall prevail in the event of any conflict.

D *Conditions concerning both buyers and sellers*

42 *Governing law:* These Conditions of Business and any amendment to them shall be governed by and interpreted and construed in accordance with English law.

43 *Jurisdiction:*

(i) 'Sotheby's' and all 'buyers' and 'sellers' (and any prospective 'buyers' or 'sellers') agree that the Courts of England are (subject to Condition 43(ii) below) to have exclusive jurisdiction to settle any dispute (including claims for set-off and counterclaims) which may arise in connection with the validity, effect, interpretation or performance of, or the legal relationships established by, these Conditions of Business or otherwise arising in connection with these Conditions of Business.

(ii) The agreement contained in Condition 43(i) above is included for the benefit of 'Sotheby's'. Accordingly, notwithstanding the exclusive agreement in Condition 43(i) above, 'Sotheby's' shall retain the right to bring proceedings in any Court which has jurisdiction by virtue of the Convention on Jurisdiction and the Enforcement of Judgements signed on 27 September 1968 (as from time to time amended and extended) or otherwise.

44 *Service of process:* All 'buyers' and 'sellers' irrevocably consent to service of process or any other documents in connection with proceedings in any Court by facsimile transmission, personal service, delivery at the last address known to us or any other usual address, mail or in any other manner permitted by English law, the law of the place of service or the law of the jurisdiction where proceedings are instituted.

45 *Photographs and illustrations:* You agree that we shall have the absolute right (on a non-exclusive basis) to photograph, illustrate or otherwise produce images of any lot consigned to us for sale. We shall retain copyright in all images created by us of any lot and shall have the right to use such images in whatever way we deem appropriate, both before and after the auction.

46 *Value added tax:* Where these Conditions of Business refer to an obligation to make payment by 'buyer' or 'seller', the 'buyer' or 'seller' (as applicable) shall be liable to pay any VAT required by law or, if applicable, any amount in lieu of VAT. Where the Conditions of Business give 'Sotheby's' a right to receive payment from 'buyer' or 'seller', such right shall include the right to receive any VAT due or, if applicable, any amount due in lieu of VAT.

47 *Copyright:* No representations or warranties are made by either the 'seller' or 'Sotheby's' as to whether any lot is subject to copyright, nor as to whether the 'buyer' acquires any copyright in any lot sold.

48 *Export /import and embargoes:* No representations or warranties are made by 'Sotheby's' or the 'seller' as to whether any lot is subject to any export restrictions from the United Kingdom or any import restrictions of any other country. Similarly, we make no representations or warranties as to whether any embargoes exist in relation to particular lots.

49 *Notices:* Any notice or other communication shall be in writing and, if sent by post, shall be deemed to have been received by the addressee on the second working day after posting or, if the addressee is outside the United Kingdom, on the fifth working day after posting. If any written notice is delivered by hand, it shall be treated as having been received at that time and, if any written notice is sent by facsimile, it shall be deemed to have been received 24 hours after sending. Any notice sent to us shall be sent to 34-35 New Bond Street, London W1A 2AA. Any notice which we send to you may be sent to your last address known to us.

50 *Severability:* In the event that any provisions of these Conditions of Business should be held unenforceable for any reason, the remaining conditions shall remain in full force and effect.

51 *Personal details:* If we so request, each of the 'buyer', the 'seller' and any bidder at auction agrees to provide (in a form acceptable to us) written confirmation of their name, permanent address, proof of identity and creditworthiness.

52 *Introductory commissions:* We reserve the right to pay out of our remuneration a fee to any third party introducing clients or property to us.

53 *Miscellaneous:*

(i) The headings and introduction to these Conditions of Business do not form part of the Conditions of Business, but are for your convenience only.

(ii) No act, failure to act or partial act by 'Sotheby's' shall be deemed a waiver of any of its rights hereunder.

(iii) The singular includes the plural and vice versa where the context requires.

(iv) These Conditions of Business shall not be assignable by the 'buyer' or the 'seller' without the prior written agreement of 'Sotheby's'. However, these Conditions of Business shall be binding on any of your successors, assigns, trustees, executors, administrators and representatives.

(v) Where terms have special meanings ascribed to them, a glossary may appear before the first lot in the relevant catalogue.

VAT INFORMATION FOR BUYERS

The following paragraphs are intended to give guidance to buyers on the VAT implications of purchasing property at Sotheby's. The information concerns the most usual circumstances (arising from the VAT rules introduced on 1 June 1995) and is not intended to be complete. In all cases the UK VAT legislation takes precedence and the VAT rates in effect on the day of the auction will be the rates charged. It should be noted that, for VAT purposes only, Sotheby's is not usually treated as an agent and most property is sold as if it is the property of Sotheby's.

In the following paragraphs, reference to VAT symbols shall mean those symbols located beside the lot number or the pre-sale estimates in the catalogue (or amending sale room notice).

1. Property with no VAT symbol

Where there is no VAT symbol, Sotheby's is able to use the Auctioneer's Margin Scheme and VAT will not normally be charged on the hammer price.

Sotheby's must bear VAT on the buyer's premium and hence will charge an amount in lieu of VAT at 17.5% on this premium. This amount will form part of the buyer's premium on our invoice and will not be separately identified.

Please see 'Exports from the European Union' for the conditions to be fulfilled before the amount in lieu of VAT in the buyer's premium may be cancelled or refunded.

(VAT-registered buyers from within the European Union (EU) should note that the amount in lieu of VAT contained within the buyer's premium cannot be cancelled or refunded by Sotheby's or HM Customs & Excise.)

(VAT-registered buyers from within the EU requiring an invoice under the normal VAT rules, instead of a margin scheme invoice, should notify the Cashier's Office or the Client Accounts Department on the day of the auction and an invoice with VAT on the hammer price will be raised. Buyers requiring reinvoicing under the normal VAT rules subsequent to a margin scheme invoice having been raised should contact the Client Accounts Department for assistance.)

2. Property with a † symbol

These items will be sold under the normal UK VAT rules and VAT will be charged at 17.5% on both the hammer price and buyer's premium.

Please see 'Exports from the European Union' for the conditions to be fulfilled before the VAT charged on the hammer price may be cancelled or refunded. Sotheby's must always charge VAT on the buyer's premium for these lots and will neither cancel nor refund the VAT charged.

(VAT-registered buyers from other European Union (EU) countries may have the VAT on the hammer price cancelled or refunded if they provide Sotheby's with their VAT registration number and evidence that the property has been removed from the UK within three months of the date of sale. A form is available from the Cashier's Office which will act as such evidence once completed by the buyer or the buyer's agent. If the shipping is undertaken by Sotheby's, no such form will be required.)

(All business buyers from outside the UK should refer to 'VAT Refunds from HM Customs & Excise' for information on how to recover VAT incurred on the buyer's premium.)

3. Property with a α symbol

Items sold to buyers whose address is in the European Union (EU) will be assumed to be remaining in the EU. The property will be invoiced as if it had no VAT symbol (see 'Property with no VAT symbol' above). However, if the property is to be exported from the EU, Sotheby's will re-invoice the property under the normal VAT rules (see 'Property sold with a † symbol' above) as requested by the seller.

Items sold to buyers whose address is outside the European Union (EU) will be assumed to be exported from the EU. The property will be invoiced under the normal VAT rules (see 'Property sold with a † symbol' above). Although the hammer price will be subject to VAT this will be cancelled or refunded upon export - see 'Exports from the European Union'. The buyer's premium will always attract VAT. However, buyers who are not intending to export their property from the EU should notify our Client Accounts Department on the day of the sale and the property will be re-invoiced showing no VAT on the hammer price (see 'Property sold with no VAT symbol' above).

4. Property sold with a ‡ or Ω symbol

These items have been imported from outside the European Union (EU) to be sold at auction under temporary importation. When Sotheby's releases such property to buyers in the UK, the buyer will become the importer and must pay Sotheby's import VAT at the following rates on both the hammer price and buyer's premium:

‡ - 5%

Ω - 17.5%

Buyers intending to take their purchased

property out of the EU should see 'Exports from the European Union'.

(VAT-registered buyers from the EU should note that the import VAT charged on property released in the UK cannot be cancelled or refunded by Sotheby's.)

(VAT-registered buyers from the UK should note that the invoice issued by Sotheby's for these items is not suitable evidence for VAT return purposes. You should confirm with the Shipping Department that Sotheby's has a record of your VAT registration number and wait for a certificate C79 to be issued by HM Customs & Excise.)

(VAT-registered buyers from other EU countries may be able to seek repayment of the import VAT paid by applying to HM Customs & Excise with a copy of the C88 import declaration available from the Shipping Department - see 'VAT Refunds from HM Customs & Excise'.)

5. Exports from the European Union

The following types of VAT may be cancelled or refunded by Sotheby's on exports made within three months of the sale date if strict conditions are met:

- the amount in lieu of VAT charged on buyer's premium for property sold under the margin scheme i.e. without a VAT symbol.

- the VAT on the hammer price for property sold under the normal VAT rules i.e. with a † symbol or a α symbol.

- the import VAT charged on hammer price and buyer's premium for property sold under temporary importation i.e. with a ‡ or a Ω symbol.

In each of the above examples, where the appropriate conditions are satisfied, no VAT will be charged if, at or before the time of invoicing, the buyer instructs Sotheby's to export the property from the EU. If such instruction is received after payment, a refund of the VAT amount will be made. If a buyer later decides not to use Sotheby's shipping services a revised invoice will be raised charging VAT.

Where the buyer carries purchases from the EU personally or uses the services of another shipper, Sotheby's will charge the VAT amount due as a deposit and refund it if the

lot has been exported within three months of the date of sale and the following conditions are met:

- For lots sold under the margin scheme (no VAT symbol) or the normal VAT rules († symbol), Sotheby's is provided with appropriate documentary proof of export from the EU. Buyers carrying their own property should obtain hand-carry papers from the Shipping Department to facilitate this process.

- For lots sold under temporary importation (‡ or Ω symbols), Sotheby's is provided with a copy of the correct paperwork duly completed and stamped by HM Customs & Excise. It is essential for shippers acting on behalf of buyers to collect copies of the original import papers from our Shipping Department. Buyers carrying their own property must obtain hand-carry papers from the Shipping Department.

Once the appropriate paperwork has been returned to Sotheby's, a refund of the VAT charge will be made. Please note, an administrative fee of £20.00 will be charged for this service.

Sotheby's is not able to cancel or refund any VAT charged on sales made to UK or EU private residents unless the lot is subject to temporary importation and the property is exported from the EU within three months of the date of sale.

Buyers intending to export lots under temporary importation (‡ or Ω symbols) should notify the Shipping Department **before** collection. Failure to do so may result in the crystallisation of the import VAT charge and Sotheby's will be unable to refund the VAT charged on deposit.

6. VAT Refunds from HM Customs & Excise

Where VAT charged cannot be cancelled or refunded by Sotheby's, it may be possible to seek repayment from HM Customs & Excise. Repayments in this manner are limited to businesses located outside the UK and may be considered for:

- VAT charged on buyer's premium on property sold under the normal VAT rules i.e. with a † or a symbol.

- import VAT charged on the hammer

price and buyer's premium for lots sold under temporary importation i.e. with a ‡ or Ω symbol.

Claim forms are available from:
HM Customs & Excise
Overseas Repayment Section
8th/13th Directive
Customs House
PO Box 34
Londonderry, BT48 7AE
Northern Ireland

Tel: (44) 1504 372727
Fax: (44) 1504 372520

SPECIALIST DEPARTMENTS

African & Oceanic Art
Jean Fritts (212) 606 7325
Jocelyne Timm 020 7293 5109
London Liaison

Antiquities
Richard M. Keresey (212) 774 5390
Jocelyne Timm 020 7293 5109
London Liaison

Arms & Armour
Frederick Wilkinson (01403) 833540
Consultant
Ian Eaves (01403) 833540
Consultant
Thomas Del Mar (01403) 833539

Art Nouveau & Art Deco
Lydia Cresswell-Jones 020 7293 5137
Philippe Garner 020 7293 5138
Senior Specialist

Books & Manuscripts
Dr. Stephen Roe 020 7293 5286
Mitzi Mina 020 7293 5893
Paul Quarrie FSA 020 7293 5300
Roger Griffiths 020 7293 5292
Charlotte Brown 020 7293 5296
Dr. Peter Beal F.B.A. 020 7293 5298
Dr. Susan Wharton 020 7293 5299
Catherine Porter 020 7293 5290
Catherine Slowther 020 7293 5291
Peter Selley 020 7293 5295
Dr. David Goldthorpe 020 7293 5303

Paris
Dr Jean-Baptiste de Proyart 33 (1) 5305 53 19

Milan
Filippo Lotti 39 (2) 295 001

British Paintings & Drawings 1500 - 1850
David Moore-Gwyn 020 7293 5406
Henry Wemyss 020 7293 5409
James Miller 020 7293 5405
Lucy Fenwick 020 7293 5408
Guy Peppiatt 020 7293 5410

Carpets
Raquel Diaz Downey 020 7293 5152

Chinese Ceramics & Works of Art
Henry Howard-Sneyd 020 7293 5147
Joe-Hynn Yang 020 7293 5148
Jing Chen 020 7293 5071

Chinese Export Porcelain
Alastair Gibson 020 7293 5145

European Ceramics
Simon Cottle 020 7293 5133
Sebastian Kuhn 020 7293 5135
Rebecca Wintgens 020 7293 5070

Paris
Peter Arney 020 7293 5134

Clocks, Watches & Barometers
Michael Turner 020 7293 5329
Jonathan Darracott 020 7293 5810
Alex Barter 020 7293 5327
Tina Millar 020 7293 5328

Geneva
Malin Miller 41 (22) 908 4856

Coins, Historical Medals & Banknotes
James Morton 020 7293 5314
Tom Eden 020 7293 5313
Paul Wood 020 7293 5317
Stephen Lloyd 020 7293 5312

Collectors
Kerry Taylor 020 7293 5464

Aeronautica
Stephen Maycock 020 7293 5206

Automobilia
Toby Wilson 020 7293 5491

Cameras & Optical Instruments
Nicholas Couts 020 7293 5318

Cars
James Morton 020 7293 5314

Costume, Textiles & Fashion
Kerry Taylor 020 7293 5464
Ann Knox 020 7293 5708

Dolls, Bears & Automata
Kerry Taylor 020 7293 5464
Ann Knox 020 7293 5708

Mechanical Music
Jon Baddeley 020 7293 5205
Catherine Southon 020 7293 5209

Motorcycles
Mike Jackson (01264) 810875
Consultant

Rock & Roll & Film Memorabilia
Stephen Maycock 020 7293 5206

Scientific & Technical Instruments
Jon Baddeley 020 7293 5205
Catherine Southon 020 7293 5209

Sporting Memorabilia
Graham Budd 020 7293 5269
Edward Playfair 020 7293 5208

Toys
Nicholas Couts 020 7293 5318

Contemporary Art
Cheyenne Westphal 020 7293 5391
Benjamin Brown 020 7293 5494
Matthew Carey-Williams 020 7293 5842

Paris
Florence de Botton 33 (1) 5305 5360

Milan
Claudia Dwek 39 (02) 2950 0250

Amsterdam
Miety Heiden 31 (20) 550 2254

European Sculpture & Works of Art
Alexander Kader 020 7293 5493
Elisabeth Mitchell 020 7293 5304
Diana Keith Neal 020 7293 5337
Senior Specialist
Elizabeth Wilson 020 7293 5321
Senior Specialist

Paris
Ulrike Goetz 33 (1) 5305 53 64

English Furniture
Simon Redburn 020 7293 5746
Fergus Lyons 020 7293 5348
Daniel Morris 020 7293 5486
Jeremy Smith 020 7293 5072

French & Continental Furniture
Mario Tavella 020 7293 5052
Maxine Fox 020 7293 5349
Patrick van der Vorst 020 7293 5733

Paris
Brice Foisil 33 (1) 5305 5301
Pierre-Francois Dayot 020 7293 5304

Zurich
Thomas Boller 41 (1) 202 0011

Milan
Francesco Morroni 39 (2) 295 00203

Amsterdam
Jan Willem van Haarem 31 (20) 550 2231

Nineteenth Century European Furniture & Works of Art
Jonathan Meyer F.R.I.C.S. 020 7293 5350
Alison Price James 020 7293 5107

Garden Statuary & Architectural Items
Jackie Rees (01403) 833560

Glass & Paperweights
Simon Cottle 020 7293 5133

Impressionist & Modern Art
Melanie Clore 020 7293 5394
Philip Hook 020 7293 5223
Helena Newman 020 7293 5397
Oliver Barker 020 7293 5392

Geneva
Guy Jennings 41 (22) 908 4834
Caroline Lang 41 (22) 908 4832

Paris
Andrew Strauss 33 (1) 5305 5355
Emmanuel Di-Donna 33 (1) 5305 5356

Milan
Claudia Dwek 39 (2) 295 00250

SPECIALIST DEPARTMENTS

Islamic & Indian Art
Marcus Fraser	020 7293 5332
Nicholas Shaw	020 7293 5154

Consultant

Indian Contemporary Paintings
Savita Apte	020 7293 5112

Consultant

Japanese Ceramics & Works of Art
Max Rutherston	020 7293 5142
Neil Davey	020 7293 5141

Senior Specialist

Jewellery
Geneva
David Bennett	41 (22) 908 4840

Consultant
Michael Hall	41 (22) 908 4843
Douglas Walker	41 (22) 908 4820
Alexandra Rhodes	41 (22) 908 4842

Senior Specialist

London
Martyn Downer	020 7293 5338
Joanna Hardy	020 7293 5310
Daniela Mascetti	020 7293 5308

Judaica
Camilla Previte	020 7293 5334

Tel Aviv
Esta Kilstein	972 (3) 560 1666

Medieval Manuscripts
Peter Kidd	020 7293 5330

Dr. Christopher de Hamel FSA
Consultant

Militaria
Gordon Gardiner	(01403) 833538

Modern British & Irish Pictures & Sculpture
Susannah Pollen	020 7293 5388
Joanna Doidge-Harrison	020 7293 5083

Musical Instruments
Tim Ingles	020 7293 5034
Graham Wells	020 7293 5342

Consultant
Paul Hayday	020 7293 5344

Music: Printed & Manuscript
Dr. Stephen Roe	020 7293 5286
Dr. J.S.E. Maguire	020 7293 5016

Nineteenth Century European Paintings & Drawings
Adrian Biddell	020 7293 5380
Tessa Kostrzewa	020 7293 5382
Claude Piening	020 7293 5658
Simon Shaw	020 7293 5479

Amsterdam
Drs. Eveline Van Oirschot	31 (20) 550 2255

Brussels
Michèle de Kerchove	32 (2) 627 7189

Madrid
Wendy Loges	34 (91) 532 6802

Milan
Dominique Reiner	39 (2) 295001

Paris
Pascale Pavageau	33 (1) 5305 5310

Zurich
Irene Stoll	41 (1) 226 2256
Sabrina Stüssi	41 (1) 226 2257
Michael Bing	41 (1) 226 2233

Old Master Paintings & Drawings
Paintings
Alexander Bell	020 7293 5420
George Gordon	020 7293 5414
Richard Charlton-Jones	020 7293 5489
Emily Black	020 7293 5415
Arabella Chandos	020 7293 5421
Letizia Treves	020 7293 5850
James Macdonald	020 7293 5887

Amsterdam
Baukje Coenen	31 (20) 550 2261
Judith Niessen	31 (20) 550 2258

Madrid
James Macdonald	34 (91) 576 5714

Milan
Alberto Chiesa	39 (2) 2950 0207

Paris
Nicolas Joly	33 (1) 5305 5341
Cécile Bouleau	33 (1) 5305 5326

Drawings
Gregory Rubinstein	020 7293 5417
Cristiana Romalli	020 7293 5419
Alexandra Chaldecott	020 7293 5333

Paintings & Drawings
Julien Stock	020 7293 5413

Oriental Manuscripts
Marcus Fraser	020 7293 5332

Photographs
Philippe Garner	020 7293 5138

Senior Specialist
Lydia Cresswell-Jones	020 7293 5137

Portrait Miniatures, Vertu & Fabergé
Haydn Williams	020 7293 5326
Julia Clarke	020 7293 5324

Munich
Heinrich Graf von Spreti	49 (89) 291 3151

Postage Stamps, Postal History & Postcards
Richard Ashton	020 7293 5224
David Wright	020 7293 5894

Prints
Jonathan Pratt	020 7293 5212
Susan Harris	020 7293 5211

Old Masters
Richard Godfrey	020 7293 5213

Russian Works of Art & Icons
Joanna Vickery	020 7293 5325
Martyn Saunders-Rawlins	020 7293 5325

Consultant

Scottish Paintings & Drawings
Grant Ford	020 7293 5497

Silver
Peter Waldron	020 7293 5104
Harry Charteris	020 7293 5106
John Webster	020 7293 5105

Amsterdam
Jacob Roosjen	31 (20) 550 2266

Heraldry Consultant
Don Victor Franco de Baux

Southeast Asian Paintings
Mok Kim Chuan	(65) 732 8239

Amsterdam
Miety Heiden	31 (20) 550 2254

Sporting Guns
Adrian Weller	(01403) 833575

Tapestries
George Hughes-Hartman	020 7293 5455

Consultant
Patrick van der Vorst	020 7293 5733

Travel Sales
Guy Peppiatt	020 7293 5410

Victorian Paintings & Drawings
Martin Gallon	020 7293 5386
Grant Ford	020 7293 5497
Simon Taylor	020 7293 5385

Senior Specialist

War Medals, Orders & Decorations
Edward Playfair	020 7293 5709
Paul Wood	020 7293 5317

Wildlife Paintings
Sally Goddard	(01403) 833569

Wine
Serena Sutcliffe, MW	020 7293 5050
Stephen Mould	020 7293 5046
Michael Egan	020 7293 5047
James Reed	020 7293 5014
Richard O'Mahony	020 7293 5048

Administration
Charles Cooke	020 7293 5041

CLIENT SERVICES

Bookshop & Mail Order Books
Clare Klos   020 7293 5404

Client Assistance
Enquiries   020 7293 5002

Catalogue Subscriptions
Katherine MacDonald   020 7293 5458

Client Accounts
Michael Hart   020 7293 5890

Sotheby's Institute of Art
Diana Keith Neal   020 7293 5337
New York
J. Thomas Savage   1 (212) 894 1111

Financial Services
Ann-Marie Jones   020 7293 5273
New York
Shelley Fischer   1 (212) 508 8061

Furniture Restoration
Roddy McVittie   (01403) 833626
New York
Alastair Colin Stair   1 (212) 860 5446

House Sales
James Miller   020 7293 5405
Harry Dalmeny   020 7293 5848
Alexandra Reece   020 7293 5711

Communications & Press
Christopher Proudlove   020 7293 5165
Amanda Stucklin   020 7293 5169

Shipping
Suzanne Swan   020 7293 5353

Tax & Heritage
James Jowitt   020 7293 5335
New York
Warren P. Weitman, Jr.   1 (212) 606 7198

Valuations
William Lucy   020 7293 5178
New York
Lindsey Pryor   1 (212) 606 7034

Photography
Rick Jenkins

Layout Editor
Cheryl Wooldridge

Colour Editor
Daniel Rodgers

Production Controller
Melanie Hall

Repro/Print
SOT/DIT

Cobra-Library, comprising 15 books illustrated by renowned CoBrA artists, including the publication Cobra by Jean Clarence Lambert.
Offered by the Belgium Associate Multiple 13,
Estimate: $1,500-2,500.

CoBrA 19th March – 11th April

SOTHEBYS.COM is delighted to announce its first sale devoted to the CoBrA movement, a powerful manifestation of bold figures set within a landscape of abstraction dominated by rapid rhythms of colour and form. Between 1948 and 1952, CoBrA, named after the three European cities that contributed to its foundation: Copenhagen, Brussels and Amsterdam, was considered one of the most fertile movements in contemporary European art.

SCOTTISH SALE 22nd March – 12th April

Following the success of its first online sale of Scottish pictures, SOTHEBYS.COM will be holding a second sale devoted to Scottish art. This will include paintings, drawings and watercolours depicting traditional scenes of the 19th century, as well as a section devoted to Modern and Contemporary Scottish Art. The sale will coincide with Sotheby's annual Scottish Sale at Hopetoun House.

John Houston, RSA
'She could have danced all night across a crowded room,' oil on canvas signed,
65 by 76in., 165 by 193cm.
Offered by Corrymella Scott Gallery
Estimate: $10,000-15,000

'Gelede' Mask, Yoruba tribe, SW Nigeria, painted wood in blue and white
25 by 42cm.
Offered by Peter Willborg
Estimate: $1,000-2,000

ART OF AFRICA 30th March – 13th April

SOTHEBYS.COM presents a special sale devoted to the traditional arts of Africa. A diverse selection of objects will be offered ranging from superb ceremonial figures to household and personal accoutrements.

WORKS OF ART BY LOUIS COMFORT TIFFANY
5th April – 19th April

This sale focuses on the work of the most influential figure in the development of American Art Nouveau movement, Louis Comfort Tiffany. Exemplifying the diversity of his production the sale will offer a selection of vases, desk sets, lamps, metalwork and ceramics.

Tiffany Favrile Amber Glass Vase, circa 1915
Estimate: $1,500-2,000

Københavnerstolen (The Copenhagen Chair), designed by Arch. Mogens Voltelen, produced by master cabinet maker Niels Vodder. 1960 version in oak and leather
Estimate: $2,000-3,000

RUSSIAN WORKS OF ART, PORTRAIT MINIATURES AND OBJECTS OF VERTU 12th April – 26th April

This auction will include a selection of Russian and Greek icons, porcelain, silver, objects of Vertu and European and American portrait miniatures of the 18th & 19th centuries.

KLASSIK: CLASSIC MODERN DANISH DESIGN
19th April – 10th May

Klassik, the leading Danish gallery for vintage furniture, celebrates its 10th Anniversary with a special online sale of extraordinary pieces collected through the past decade. The sale will include a wide range of specially selected objects dating from 1930 to 1960. All items in this sale will be on view at Klassik's Copenhagen gallery for the duration of the sale.

FINE ART · DECORATIVE ARTS & ANTIQUES · JEWELLERY & WATCHES · BOOKS · COLLECTABLES

Click on Current Special Auctions to find these extraordinary collections. Sotheby's and its Associate Dealers bring thousands of lots in hundreds of collecting categories together for auction only at SOTHEBYS.COM. Click on "Subscribe" to receive advance invitations to bid on the objects that interest you.

Austrian Enamel Miniature Epergne, circa 1900
Estimate: $1,000-1,500

INTERNATIONAL OFFICES

UNITED KINGDOM AND IRELAND

SALE ROOMS

London
34-35 New Bond Street
London W1A 2AA
and Bloomfield Place
(off New Bond Street)
Telephone: 020 7293 5000
Fax: 020 7293 5989

Sotheby's South
Timothy Wonnacott, FRICS
Chairman
Alistair Morris, FRICS
Managing Director
Mark Newstead
UK Regional Director
Summers Place
Billingshurst
Sussex RH14 9AD
Telephone: (01403) 833500
Fax: (01403) 833699

REGIONAL REPRESENTATIVES

Home Counties
John Hudson
Telephone: 020 7293 5897
Fax: 020 7293 5934

Kent & East Sussex
Lucy Sclater
Telephone/Fax: (01273) 891030

Cotswolds, South Wales & South West
John Harvey
18 Imperial Square
Cheltenham
Gloucestershire GL50 1QZ
Telephone: (01242) 510500
Fax: (01242) 250252

Charles Hignett
Bath, Somerset
Telephone: (01225) 840101
Fax: (01225) 840696

Devon & Cornwall
The Hon. Mrs. d'Erlanger
Hensleigh Cottage
Hensleigh
Tiverton
Devon EX16 5NH
Telephone: (01884) 243 663
Fax: (01884) 258 692

Elizabeth Fortescue
Lostwithiel, Cornwall
Telephone/Fax: (01208) 871133

Wessex
Colin Thompson
Jeremy Waite
Cheviot House
69-73 Castle Street
Salisbury, Wiltshire SP1 3SP
Telephone: (01722) 330793
Fax: (01722) 330982

East Anglia & The Midlands
Chantal Langley
David Asher
The Railway Station
Green Road
Newmarket
Suffolk CB8 9TW
Telephone: (01638) 561426
Fax: (01638) 560094

The Lord Cranworth
Woodbridge, Suffolk
Telephone: (01473) 735581
Fax: (01473) 738278

Sara Foster
Fakenham, Norfolk
Telephone: (01328) 700032
Fax: (01328) 700155

Northamptonshire
Mary Miller
Towcester
Northamptonshire
Telephone: (01327) 860020
Fax: (01327) 860612

North West & North Wales
Gareth Williams
The Hon. Rose Paterson
Lightfoot Street
Hoole, Chester
Cheshire CH2 3AD
Telephone: (01244) 315531
Fax: (01244) 346984

The Marchioness of Linlithgow
Powys, Wales
Telephone: (01691) 648646
Fax: (01691) 648664

Nottinghamshire & Derbyshire
Mark Newstead
Nottingham
Telephone/Fax: (0115) 966 5478

Lord Ralph Kerr
Melbourne, Derbyshire
Telephone: (01638) 561426
Fax: (01638) 560094

Yorkshire
John Phillips, ARICS
8-12 Montpellier Parade
Harrogate
North Yorkshire HG1 2TJ
Telephone: (01423) 501466
Fax: (01423) 520501

Northern England
Matthew Festing, OBE
Unit 12A,
Stocksfield Hall, Stocksfield
Northumberland NE43 7TN
Telephone: (01661) 843 320
Fax: (01661) 843 969

Judith Heelis
Appleby, Cumbria
Telephone/Fax: (017683) 52806

Channel Islands
Clare d'Abo
Telephone: 020 7293 5363
Fax: 020 7293 5907

Scotland & Borders
John Robertson
Emily Pelham Burn
Georgiana Bruce
112 George Street
Edinburgh EH2 4LH
Telephone: (0131) 226 7201
Fax: (0131) 226 6866

Anthony Weld Forester
130 Douglas Street
Glasgow G2 4HF
Telephone: (0141) 221 4817
Fax: (0141) 204 2502

Northern Ireland
William Montgomery
The Estate Office
Grey Abbey
Newtownards
Co. Down BT22 2QA
Telephone: (028) 4278 8668
Fax: (028) 4278 8652

Ireland
Arabella Bishop
Anne Dillon
16 Molesworth Street
Dublin 2, Ireland
Telephone: 00 353 1 671 1786
Fax: 00 353 1 679 7844

EUROPE AND MIDDLE EAST

AUSTRIA

Andrea Jungmann
Palais Breuner, Singerstrasse 16
1010 Vienna
Telephone: 43 (1) 512 4772/3 &
513 3774
Fax: 43 (1) 513 4867

BELGIUM

Count Hubert d'Ursel
Monique Bréhier
32 rue Jacques Jordaens
1000 Brussels
Telephone: 32 (2) 648 0080
Fax: 32 (2) 648 0757

CZECH REPUBLIC

Filip Marco
Ungelt-Tynsky Dvur
Mala Stupartska 5
110 00 Prague 1
Telephone/Fax: 42 (02) 2482 6538

DENMARK

Baroness Hanne Wedell-
Wedellsborg
Bredgade 6, 1260 Copenhagen K
Telephone: 45 (33) 135556
Fax: 45 (33) 930119

FINLAND

Claire Svartström
Bernhardinkatu 1B
00 130 Helsinki
Telephone: 358 (9) 622 1558
Fax: 358 (9) 680 1208

INTERNATIONAL OFFICES

FRANCE

Paris
Princesse de Beauvau Craon
P.D.G., France
Deputy Chairman, Europe
Peter Arney
Managing Director
Jeremy Durack
Finance & Operations Director

76 rue du Faubourg St. Honoré
75008 Paris
Telephone: 33 (1) 53 05 53 05
Fax: 33 (1) 47 42 22 32

Bordeaux
Alain de Baritault
Telephone/Fax: 33 (5) 56 58 72 04

Lyon
Albert de Franclieu
Telephone/Fax: 33 (4) 76 07 15 52

Montpellier
Béatrice Viennet
Telephone: 33 (4) 67 24 95 72
Fax: 33 (4) 67 24 93 52

Strasbourg
Marie-France Ludmann
Telephone/Fax: 33 (3) 88 60 00 61

GERMANY

Frankfurt
Dr. Philipp Herzog von
Württemberg
Managing Director-Germany
Nina Buhne
Mendelssohnstrasse 66
D-60325 Frankfurt-am-Main
Telephone: 49 (69) 74 07 87
Fax: 49 (69) 74 69 01

Munich
Heinrich Graf von Spreti
President-Germany
Odeonsplatz 16
D-80539 München
Telephone: 49 (89) 291 31 51
Fax: 49 (89) 299 271

Cologne
Ursula Niggemann
Vice President-Germany
Jörg-Michael Bertz
Vice President-Germany
St. Apern - Strasse 17-21
D-50667 Köln
Telephone: 49 (221) 20 7170
Fax: 49 (221) 257 4359

Hamburg
Axel Benz
Tesdorpfstrasse 22
D-20148 Hamburg
Telephone: 49 (40) 44 40 80
Fax: 49 (40) 410 70 82

ISRAEL

Rivka Saker
46 Rothschild Boulevard
Tel Aviv 66883
Telephone: 972 (3) 5601666
Fax: 972 (3) 5608111

ITALY

Filippo Lotti
Managing Director

Milan
Filippo Lotti
Claudia Dwek
Deputy Chairman
Palazzo Broggi
Via Broggi 19, 20129 Milan
Telephone: 39 0 (2) 29 5001
Fax: 39 0 (2) 29 518595

Rome
Luisa Lepri
Director
Silvia Geddes da Filicaia
Piazza di Spagna 90
00187 Rome
Telephone: 39 0 (6) 699 41791
Fax: 39 0 (6) 679 6167

Florence
Clementina Bartolini Salimbeni
Telephone: 39 0 (55) 247 9021
Fax: 39 0 (55) 247 9563

Turin
Laura Russo
Director
Corso Galileo, Ferraris 18B
10121 Turin
Telephone: 39 0 (11) 544898
Fax: 39 0 (11) 547675

LUXEMBOURG

Please refer all enquiries to
Count Hubert d'Ursel
in the Brussels Office
Telephone: 32 (2) 648 0080
Fax: 32 (2) 648 0757

MONACO

Mark Armstrong
B.P.45, Le Sporting d'Hiver
Place du Casino
MC 98001 Monaco Cedex
Telephone: 377 (93) 30 88 80
Fax: 377 (93) 25 24 98

NETHERLANDS

John L. van Schaik
Managing Director
Patrick van Maris
Deputy Managing Director
De Boelelaan 30
1083 HJ Amsterdam
Telephone: 31 (20) 550 22 00
Fax: 31 (20) 550 22 22

NORWAY

Ingeborg Astrup
Bjørnveien 42, 0774 Oslo
Telephone: 47 (22) 1472 82
Fax: 47 (22) 49 38 36

SPAIN

Madrid
Carmen Araoz de Urquijo
Serrano 32, 2° Int-Dcha
28001 Madrid
Telephone: 34 (91) 576 5714
Fax: 34 (91) 781 2490

SWEDEN

Stockholm
Lars Nedergaard
Arsenalsgatan 6
S-111 47 Stockholm
Telephone: 46 (8) 679 5478
Fax: 46 (8) 611 4826

Gothenburg
Viviann Kempe
Villa Thalatta
James Keillers Väg 12
S - 429 43 SÄRÖ
Telephone: 46 (31) 937 150
Fax: 46 (31) 937 550

South Sweden
Baroness Catharina von
Blixen-Finecke
Näsbyholm Säteri
S - 274 94 SKURUP
Telephone: 46 (411) 43981
Fax: 46 (411) 43982

SWITZERLAND

Guy Jennings
Chairman

Geneva
Peter-Paul Guthman
13 Quai du Mont Blanc
CH -1201 Geneva
Telephone: 41 (22) 908 4800
Fax: 41 (22) 908 4804

Zurich
Paul Mack
Gessnerallee 1
CH - 8021 Zurich
Telephone: 41 (1) 226 2200
Fax: 41 (1) 226 2201

Lugano
Iris Fabbri
Piazza Riforma 4
CH-6900 Lugano
Telephone: 41 (91) 9238562
Fax: 41 (91) 9238563

INTERNATIONAL OFFICES

AFRICA

SOUTH AFRICA

Johannesburg
Stephan Welz
Managing Director
13 Biermann Avenue
Rosebank
Johannesburg 2196
Telephone: 27 (11) 880 3125/9
Fax: 27 (11) 880 2656

Cape Town
86 Hout Street
Cape Town 8001
Telephone: 27 (21) 423 4728
Fax: 27 (21) 424 8700

ASIA

CHINA

Wang Jie
Dynasty Business Centre
Room 401
457 Wu Lu Mu Qi Road (N)
Shanghai 200040, PRC
Tel: 86 (21) 6249 7450
Fax: 86 (21) 6249 7451

HONG KONG

Henry Howard-Sneyd
Managing Director, China and Southeast Asia
5/F Standard Chartered Bank Building
4-4A Des Voeux Road Central
Hong Kong
Telephone: (852) 2524 8121
Fax: (852) 2810 6238

INDONESIA

Martina Sudwikatmono*
Mitra Bldg., 3rd Floor
JL. Gatot Subroto, Kav. 21
Jakarta 12930
Telephone: 622 (1) 522 0156
Fax: 622 (1) 522 0074

JAPAN

Tetsuji Shibayama
President
Fuerte Kojimachi Bldg. 3F
1-7 Kojimachi
Chiyoda-ku, Tokyo 102
Telephone: 81 (3) 3230 2755
Fax: 81 (3) 3230 2754

KOREA

c/o Hong Kong Office
Telephone: (852) 2524 8121
Fax: (852) 2810 6238

MALAYSIA

Walter Cheah
Managing Director
25 Jalan Pudu Lama
50200 Kuala Lumpur
Telephone: 60 (3) 230 0319
Fax: 60 (3) 230 6833

SINGAPORE

Esther Seet
Managing Director
1 Cuscaden Road
01- 01 The Regent Singapore
Singapore 249715
Telephone: (65) 732 8239
Fax: (65) 737 0295

TAIWAN, R.O.C.

Bobbie Hu
Chairman and Managing Director
1st Floor, No. 77
Sec. 1, An Ho Road
Taipei, Taiwan, R.O.C.
Telephone: 886 (2) 2755 2906
Fax: 886 (2) 2709 3949

THAILAND

Rika Dila
Sotheby's Representative
Sukhothai Hotel
13/3 South Sathorn Rd
Bangkok 10120
Thailand
Telephone: (662) 286 0788
& (662) 286 0789
Fax: (662) 286 0787

AUSTRALIA

Justin Miller
Chairman
Paul Sumner
Managing Director
Melbourne
926 High Street, Armadale
Melbourne, Victoria 3143
Telephone: 61 (3) 9509 2900
Fax: 61 (3) 9563 5067

Sydney
Queen's Court, Level 1
118-122 Queen Street
Woollahra
New South Wales 2025
Telephone: 61 (2) 9362 1000
Fax: 61 (2) 9362 1100

LATIN AMERICA

ARGENTINA

Buenos Aires
Adela MacKinlay de Casal
Avenida Alvear 1640 (P.B.)
1014 Buenos Aires
Telephone: (541) 14 814 4454
Fax: (541) 14 814 5033

BRAZIL

Rio de Janeiro
Katia Mindlin Leite Barbosa‡
Caixa Postal 62619
Rio de Janeiro
RJ CEP 22250-970
Telephone: 55 (21) 553 1946
Fax: 55 (21) 553 4594
Heloise Guinle‡
Estrada da Gavea 611
Bloco 1, Apt 2503
São Conrado
22610-000 Gavea
Rio de Janeiro
Telephone: 55 (21) 322 4500
Fax: 55 (21) 322 6397

São Paulo
Pedro Corrêa do Lago‡
Rua João Cachoeira 267
São Paulo SP CEP 04535-010
Telephone: 55 (11) 3167 0066
Fax: 55 (11) 3168 1559

MEXICO

Mexico City
Ana Yturbe de Sepulveda
Campos Eliseos 325-5 Polanco
Mexico 11560 D.F.
Telephone: (525) 281 2100
(525) 281 2200
Fax: (525) 280 7136

Luis C. Lopez Morton‡
Jewelery Consultant
Monte Athos 179
Lomas Virreyes
C.P. 11000
Mexico, D.F.
Telephone: (525) 520 5005
(525) 502 9936
Fax: (525) 540 3213

Monterrey
Barbara Perusquia de Lobeira‡
Via Triumphalis 127 PTE.
Fuentes Del Valle
Monterrey 66220, N.L.
Telephone: (528) 129 5081
Fax: (528) 378 2432

VENEZUELA

Diana Boccardo
Edf. Torresamán, Ofc. 91
Avenida Romulo Gallegos con calle El Carmen
Los Dos Caminos
Caracas, Venezuela
Telephone: (582) 234 8298
Fax: (582) 237 3920

HEADQUARTERS

1334 York Avenue
New York, New York 10021
Telephone: (212) 606 7000
Fax: (212) 606 7107
(212) 606 7016 (Bids only)

OFFICES AND ASSOCIATES

U.S.A.

Atlanta
Virginia Groves Beach†
77 West Paces Ferry
Atlanta, Georgia 30305
Telephone: (404) 355 7225
Fax: (404) 355 8599

* *Associate of Sotheby's*
† *International Representative*
‡ *Consultant*

INTERNATIONAL OFFICES

Baltimore
Aurelia Bolton*
Elizabeth Schroeder*
P.O. Box 250
Riderwood, Maryland 21139
Telephone: (410) 252 4600
Fax: (410) 561 9738

Chicago
215 West Ohio Street
Chicago, Illinois 60610
Telephone: (312) 396 9599
Fax: (312) 396 9598
Helyn D. Goldenberg
Chairman, Midwest
Larry Sirolli
Managing Director
Cassie Spencer
Trusts & Estates
Eve Reppen Rogers
Jewelry
Richard T. Nelson
Furniture & Decorative Art
Gary F. Metzner
Fine Arts
Marcus Tremonto
Art Nouveau & Art Deco
Michael Davis
Paul Hart
Wine
Marjorie S. Susman†

Dallas
Serena Ritch*
Nancy Strauss Halbreich*
2800 Routh Street, Suite 140
Dallas, Texas 75201
Telephone: (214) 871 1056
Fax: (214) 871 1057

Delaware
Barbara C. Riegel*
P.O. Box 67
Montchanin
Delaware 19710
Telephone: (302) 652 6570
Fax: (302) 652 6575

Honolulu
Andrea Song Gelber*
P.O. Box 177
Honolulu, Hawaii 96810
Telephone: (808) 732 0122
Fax: (808) 732 0122

Houston
2001 Kirby Drive, Suite 805
Houston, Texas 77019
Telephone: (713) 524 0044
Fax: (713) 520 1602

Los Angeles
9665 Wilshire Blvd.
Beverly Hills
California 90212
Telephone: (310) 274 0340
Fax: (310) 274 0899
Andrea L. Van de Kamp
Chairman, West Coast
Richard S. Wolf
Managing Director, West Coast
August O. Uribe
Director, Fine Arts, West Coast
Lisa Hubbard
International Jewelry
Peggy Gotlieb
Director, Jewelry
Katherine Watkins
Director, Decorative Arts

McLeod
Kathryn Wilmerding Heminway
Bar 20 Ranch
West Bouler Reserve
McLeod, Montana 59052
Telephone: (406) 222 9399
Fax: (406) 222 0051

Miami
Douglas Entrance
800 Douglas Road
Suite 125
Coral Gables, Florida 33134
Telephone: (305) 448 7882
Fax: (305) 448 7168
Axel Stein
Director
Tracy Sherman
Jewelry
Dolores C. Smithies‡

Minneapolis/St. Paul
Laura MacLennan
2030 Foshay Tower
821 Marquette Avenue
Minneapolis
Minnesota 55402
Telephone: (612) 332 8938
Fax: (612) 332 7456

Naples
Barbara Deisroth
Telephone/Fax: (813) 261 6787

New England
William S. Cottingham
Allison Neder
Director
Patricia Ward
Representative
67½ Chestnut St.
Boston, Massachusetts 02108
Telephone: (617) 367 6323
Fax: (617) 367 4888

New York City
Barbara Cates*
Suzette de Marigny Smith*
Brooke Douglass de Ocampo*
Lee Copley Thaw†
Barbara de Portago‡
Telephone: (212) 606 7442

North Carolina
Robert V. Ruggiero‡
597 Fog Hollow Cove
Clyde, North Carolina 28721
Telephone: (828) 627 6004
Fax: (828) 627 2059

Palm Beach
225 Peruvian Avenue
Palm Beach, Florida 33480
Telephone: (561) 833 2582
Fax: (561) 655 4583
David G. Ober
Chairman, Southeast
Hope P. Kent*
Louis J. Gartner*

Philadelphia
Angela Hudson
Director
Wendy Foulke
18 Haverford Station Road
Haverford, PA 19041
Telephone: (610) 649 2600
Fax: (610) 649 7995

Richmond
Virginia Guest Valentine†
Telephone: (212) 606 7442
Fax: (804) 353 0575

San Francisco
Jennifer Seymour Foley
Mrs. Prentis Cobb Hale*
Mrs. John N. Rosekrans†
214 Grant Avenue, Suite 350
San Francisco
California 94108
Telephone: (415) 772 9028
Fax: (415) 772 9031

Santa Barbara
Robin C. Woodworth*
661 Corte de Quintero
Camarillo, California 93010
Telephone/Fax: (805) 485 6120

Seattle
Catherine Vare
110 Union Street
Suite 300
Seattle, Washington 98101
Telephone: (206) 667 9575
Fax: (206) 667 9576

St. Louis
Telephone: (312) 396 9599

Washington, D.C.
Sidney Ferguson‡

BERMUDA

William S. Cottingham
c/o Margot Cooper
P.O. Box WK 99
Warwick, Bermuda
Telephone: (441) 295 6891
(441) 295 7392

CANADA

Michina Pope
Internet Sales
Business Development
Beverly Schaeffer
Shawna White
Canadian Art
9 Hazelton Avenue
Toronto, Ontario M5R 2E1
Telephone: (416) 926 1774
Fax: (416) 926 9179

Sotheby's South

Sotheby's South is Britain's largest auction house outside London, holding more than 150 sales a year. Buyers from all over the world congregate at Sotheby's South to view the spectrum of arts and antique on offer. While sales often include precious and rare pictures and objects, fascinating items can be discovered for as little as £200.

For a full sale calendar, information about viewing times, or catalogue subscriptions, please call 01403 833500.

SOTHEBY'S SOUTH

Summers Place, Billingshurst, West Sussex, RH14 9AD
www.sothebys.com

SOTHEBY'SOUTH

Sale Title
Scottish Pictures
Hopetoun House

Date
9 April 2001

Sale Code
"MATADOR" L01140

Please mail or fax until 6 April
Sotheby's Bid Department
34-35 New Bond Street, London W1A 2AA
For Bids only: Tel 020 7293 5283
Fax 020 7293 6255

Please mail or fax from 7 April
Hopetoun House, South Queensferry,
West Lothian EH30 9SL
Sotheby's Direct Lines:
Telephone: 0131 331 4395/2612
Fax 0131 331 2268

Important
Please bid on my behalf at the above sale for the following Lot(s) up to the hammer price(s) mentioned below. These bids are to be executed as cheaply as is permitted by other bids or reserves and in an amount up to but not exceeding the specified amount. The auctioneer may open the bidding on any lot by placing a bid on behalf of the seller. The auctioneer may further bid on behalf of the seller up to the amount of the reserve by placing responsive or consecutive bids for a lot.

I agree to be bound by the Conditions of Business. If any bid is successful, I agree to pay a buyer's premium on the hammer price at the rate stated in the Guide for Prospective Buyers in the catalogue. Please refer to the "VAT information for Buyers" in the catalogue regarding any VAT, or amounts in lieu of VAT, which may be due on the buyer's premium and the hammer price.

Methods of Payment
Sotheby's welcomes the following methods of payment, most of which will facilitate immediate release of your purchases. Please see the Guide for Prospective Buyers section in the sale catalogue for further details regarding payment methods.

Wire Transfer to our Bank
Barclays Bank plc, 50 Pall Mall, London
SW1A 1QA
Sort Code: 20-67-59 Account No. 60163058
Sterling Cash
Sterling Bankers Draft
(Drawn on a recognised UK bank)

ABSENTEE BID FORM

Name (please print or type)   Date

Sotheby's Client Account No., if known

Address

                                               Postcode

Telephone/Home   Business

Fax   Email

VAT No.

Signed   Date

Credit Cards
Mastercard, Visa & Eurocard **(Subject to 1.5% service charge)**
Please charge my Credit/Debit card for my purchases in this sale

Name on Card

Type of Card

Card Number

Expiry Date   Issue Number

Payments exceeding £20,000 can only be made by the cardholder in person.

Please write clearly and submit your bids as early as possible

Lot Number	Title/Description	Sterling Price (excluding premium and VAT)
		£
		£
		£
		£
		£

Sterling Cheque
(Drawn on a UK bank) We require seven days to clear a cheque without a letter of guarantee from your bank, or a pre-arranged cheque acceptance account. Forms to facilitate this are available from the Cashiers office.
Debit Cards
Delta, Barclays Connect & Switch

Important Notice
Please indicate on the bidding slip or separately if you wish your purchases to be held in Glasgow or sent to Edinburgh or London for collection (See Important Information for Buyers)

Please complete Shipping Instructions on reverse

GUIDE FOR ABSENTEE BIDDERS

Absentee Bids

If you are unable to attend an auction in person, you may give Sotheby's Bid department instructions to bid on your behalf. We will then try to purchase the lot of your choice for the lowest price possible, and never for more than the top amount you indicate. This service is free and confidential. Please note: Although we will make every effort, Sotheby's will not be responsible for error or failure to execute bids. Absentee bids, when placed by telephone, are accepted only at the caller's risk and must be confirmed by letter, or fax. Fax number for bids only: 020 7293 6255 until Friday 6 April. Thereafter, Hopetoun: 0131 331 2268.

Using the Absentee Bid Form

Please use the form provided and be sure to record accurately the lot numbers, descriptions and top hammer price you are willing to pay for each lot. "Buy" or unlimited bids will not be accepted. Alternative bids can be placed by using the word "OR" between lot numbers. Bids must be placed in the same order as the lots appear in the catalogue.

Each absentee bid form should contain bids for one sale only; the sale number and code name should appear at the top of the form. Please place your bids as early as possible. In the event of identical bids, the earliest received will take precedence. Where appropriate your bids will be rounded down to the nearest amount consistent with the Auctioneer's bidding increments.

Successful Bids

Successful bidders will receive an invoice detailing their purchases and giving instructions for payment and clearance of goods. Unsuccessful absentee bidders will be advised.

Postal and Telephone Bidders on Furniture and Large Objects

Bidders on large objects are advised to check on the afternoon of the sale whether they have been successful. Successful buyers of large objects are earnestly requested to arrange early collection of their goods. Please see the Important Notice at the front of the catalogue for details.

Sotheby's Client Account Number

I do/do not require a quotation before the shipment is processed *(delete as applicable)*

Insurance

Please arrange/do not arrange transit insurance. All lots will be insured unless you indicate otherwise.

Postal Consignments only

Please indicate below either
1. Do not remove frames.
    (Glass will be discarded).
2. Remove frames.
NB items valued in excess of £1,000 or weighing more than 2kg including packing, cannot be sent by this method.

Licences

Should any of my purchases require a licence prior to export, I hereby authorise you to submit the application on my behalf, and when granted, despatch the goods via your nominated shipper.

Signed
_____

SHIPPING INSTRUCTIONS

Please complete this form and we shall arrange for the despatch of all your purchases through one of our nominated shipping agents, at your expense.

Select a method of despatch

☐	☐	☐	☐	☐	☐
Commercial Courier	Air Freight	Registered Post	Sea Freight	Road	Sotheby's to Select

Delivery Address

_____

_____

Telephone	Fax	E-mail

Credit or Debit Card details (for Shipment only)

Name on Card

_____

Card Number _____ Expiry Date

If you do not give card details, shipment will not be processed until the payment has been received by the nominated shipper

Invoice Address *(if different from delivery address)*

_____

_____

Telephone	Fax	E-mail

I am VAT Registered   Y/N   VAT Number

Dated

CATALOGUE SUBSCRIPTION ORDER FORM

Your private view of some of the world's most beautiful objects

All catalogues are richly illustrated in colour and are indispensable reference guides full of fascinating information. Catalogues will be sent to you automatically as soon as they become available. A subscription lasts for 12 months and can be started at any time. Please place a tick next to the specialised catalogue you wish to receive. ✓

To order please post or fax this form to
Sotheby's
34-35 New Bond Street
London W1A 2AA
Tel: 020 7293 6444
Fax: 020 7293 5909

○

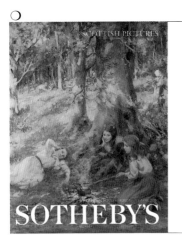

Scotland
Scottish & Sporting Paintings

Ref. L069
1 Catalogue

Price
UK / US / EUR £15
Rest of World £21

○

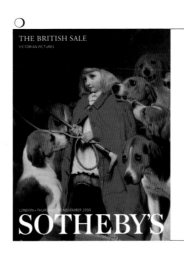

London
Victorian Paintings

Ref. L067
6 Catalogues

Price
UK / US / EUR £90
Rest of World £126

○

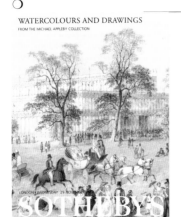

London
British Drawings & Watercolours

Ref. L063
5 Catalogues

Price
UK / US / EUR £69
Rest of World £97

○

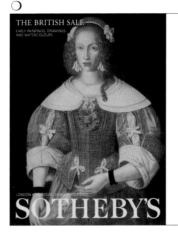

London
British Paintings 1500 to 1850

Ref. L062
5 Catalogues

Price
UK / US / EUR £84
Rest of World £118

○ Please send me a free copy of Sotheby's Catalogue and Publications Guide giving details of all subscription categories, other publications and services

Method of payment

○ Visa   ○ MasterCard   ○ American Express   ○ Cheque
(Please make all cheques payable to Sotheby's)

CARD NUMBER

EXPIRY DATE

CARD MEMBER SIGNATURE

Do you already subscribe to Sotheby's Catalogues?   ○ Yes   ○ No

Send catalogues to

SURNAME   FIRST NAME

ADDRESS

                                 POST CODE

PHONE   FAX

E-MAIL

SOTHEBY'S EUROPE

Board of Directors

Henry Wyndham
Chairman

Princess de Beauvau Craon
Deputy Chairman

Melanie Clore
Deputy Chairman

Guy Jennings
Deputy Chairman

Tobias Meyer
Deputy Chairman

The Hon James Stourton
Deputy Chairman

James Miller
Deputy Chairman UK

Robin Woodhead
Chief Executive

George Bailey
Managing Director

Simon Taylor
Deputy Managing Director

Alex Bell

Philip Hook

Paul Mack

Serena Sutcliffe, M.W.

Mario Tavella

Senior Directors

Peter Arney
Richard Ashton
Jonathan Baddeley
Adrian Biddell
Michael Bing
Thomas Boller
Florence de Botton
Richard Charlton-Jones
Natacha Chiaramonte
Tom Christopherson
Jennifer Conner
Jeff Cook
Jackie Coulter
Neil Davey
Marie-Odile Deutsch
Jeremy Durack
Hubert d'Ursel
Claudia Dwek
Marcus Fraser
Martin Gallon
Philippe Garner
George Gordon
Roger Griffiths
Michael Hall
Nicolas Joly
James Jowitt
Diana Keith Neal
Marcus Linell
William Lucy
Jonathan Massey
Patrick van Maris

David Moore-Gwyn
Alistair Morris
James Morton
Helena Newman
Ursula Niggemann
Stefano Papi
Susannah Pollen
Jonathan Pratt
Christopher Proudlove
Jean-Baptiste de Proyart
Paul Quarrie
Alexandra Rhodes
Dr. Stephen Roe
Charles Rolandi
Rivka Saker
Lucian Simmons
Margaret Southern
Heinrich Graf v. Spreti
Julien Stock
Irene Stoll
Andrew J. Strauss
John Van Schaik
Peter Waldron
Sara Webb
Henry Wemyss
Cheyenne Westphal
Elisabeth Wilson
Patricia Wong
Tim Wonnacott
Philipp von Württemburg

Non-Executive Directors

Earl of Arundel
Peter Blond
Sir Nicholas Henderson,
G.C.M.G., K.C.V.O.
The Hon. Simon Howard
Lord Nicholas Gordon Lennox,
K.C.M.G., K.C.V.O.
The Hon. Sir Charles Morrison
Alexander Russell

SOTHEBY'S HOLDINGS, INC.

Board of Directors

Michael I. Sovern
Chairman

Max M. Fisher
Vice Chairman

Marquess of Hartington
Deputy Chairman

William F. Ruprecht
President and Chief Executive Officer

Robin Woodhead
Executive Vice President and Chief Executive, Europe and Asia

The Hon.
Conrad M. Black, P.C., O.C.

The Viscount Blakenham

George Blumenthal

Steven B. Dodge

Dr. Henry G. Jarecki

Henry R. Kravis

Jeffrey H. Miro

Brian S. Posner

Sharon Percy Rockefeller

Robert S. Taubman

Advisory Board, Sotheby's Holdings, Inc.

Ambassador Walter J.P. Curley
Chairman

Giovanni Agnelli

Lodewijk J.R. de Vink

Ann Getty

Alexis Gregory

Alexander M. Laughlin

Sir Q.W. Lee

John L. Marion

The Rt. Hon.
Sir Angus Ogilvy, K.C.V.O.

Carroll Petrie

Carol Price

Baron Hans Heinrich
Thyssen-Bornemisza de Kaszon